D1297415

GANBARE!

An Example of Japanese Spirit

ALSO BY PATSY SUMIE SAIKI

Early Japanese Immigrants in Hawai'i
Japanese Women in Hawai'i: The First 100 Years
Travel Is Not Just for Sightseeing: Insightseeing
Sachie: A Daughter of Hawai'i

GANBARE!

AN EXAMPLE OF JAPANESE SPIRIT

Patsy Sumie Saiki

MUTUAL PUBLISHING

This book is dedicated to
Mae, Kathleen, Kenneth and Dennis
who made motherhood
a loving, satisfying experience.

COPYRIGHT ©1982 Patsy Sumie Saiki

Library of Congress Catalog Card Number: 2004106326

First Printing—July, 2004
1 2 3 4 5 6 7 8 9 0

Cover Photo Credits: National Archives photo no. 210-G-C840
Origami crane: Andrew Jaster
Design by Wanni Cheung

ISBN 1-56647-678-X

Mutual Publishing
1215 Center Street, Suite 210
Honolulu, Hawai'i 96816
Ph: 808-732-1709
Fax: 808-734-4094
mutual@mutualpublishing.com
www.mutualpublishing.com

Printed in Taiwan

Contents

GANBARE! by Patsy S. Saiki, will help young people to remember the little known story of how some 1,500 of Hawai'i's Japanese (many of them Americans) were plucked from their homes and installed in internment camps during World War II. It recounts stories of how one generation of immigrants and their children acted when they experienced becoming exiles from a land they loved so much. Deprived of their "home" and their freedom, they kept asking, in vain, "We experience the penalty of being Japanese, but what is our crime?"

Patsy Saiki has dramatically told their stories, not so much in terms of injustice and suffering, but their personal growth. Here are internees who first lived in fear and anxiety. They resigned themselves to authorities without question. With no future on the horizon, they took flight from themselves and thereby experienced the poverty of human existence. Yet they could never forget the loved ones left behind. Their deepest yearning was for "home," not their place of residence but for an island community called Hawai'i. These and other experiences kept the spirit of *Ganbare! Ganbare!* alive—keep going, keep trying!

Gradually they were able to examine their human condition which raised questions of conscience, values and relationships. They questioned from the depths of their boundless spirit and thereby embraced the adventure of being. Through their caring and sharing, they learned to accept themselves as those who do not belong to themselves alone but to others as well. They also remembered an ancient Japanese folk wisdom: "Seven times down, eight times up."

Professor Mitsuo Aoki
Department of Religion, University of Hawai'i

ACKNOWLEDGMENTS

I am deeply indebted to the following:

First, to the National and to the Honolulu Chapter of the Japanese American Citizens League (JACL) for kindling my interest in the internment issue. I had known about the internment and even had relatives who were interned. When they returned to Hawai'i, however, they studiously avoided the topic of camp life. Even today, forty years later, some refuse to speak of their experiences.

I remember Tachikawa Japanese Language School had been closed after Dec. 7, 1941, and Mr. Adachi, a gentle and patient teacher, had disappeared. When next I saw him, several years later, he was peddling fish from a decrepit truck. I innocently wondered why. Later, I learned Japanese language schools could not be re-opened until long after the end of the war, and highly educated professionals who returned from concentration camps had to take any job to earn a living.

Then thanks go to ex-internees Genpachi Tsushima, reporter for the *Hawaii Times,* for providing me a list of the internees, and to Tsuneichi Yamamoto, editor emeritus of the *Hawaii Hochi,* for informing me as to who was still alive after 40 years. They saved me time and energy.

Many people generously shared their time, information, expertise, experiences, diaries, pictures, sketches and books. Without their cooperation and stories, this book would not have been possible. I regret I was unable to use more of their stories.

I am grateful to Mrs. Kumaji Furuya and to Mrs. Miya Soga for allowing me to use some of the material in the books *Haisho Tenten* and *Tessaku Seikatsu* (in Japanese); and to Dr. Kazuo Miyamoto, author of *Hawai'i: End of the Rainbow* for information, suggestions and corrections.

Frances Jackson, librarian at the University of Hawai'i, made material in the Hawai'i War Records Depository readily available. She was always accommodating and gracious.

Bertram Komenaka reproduced many shots of camp photographs as "my contribution to the history of these four years."

For presenting the officers' perspective of camp life, I am grateful to Col. David R. Dingeman, U.S. Army (Ret.); Col. Carl F. Eifler, U.S. Army (Ret.); and Col. Siegfried H. Spillner, U.S. Army (Ret.), all of whom served at Sand Island or at Honouliuli, Oʻahu.

Thanks also to Terry and Harold Fukuoka, the patient and meticulous typesetters who suggested type and size of the finished product, and to Hirata-Nonaka for their suggestions in art and layout.

Finally, thanks go to Ken Hiraki for suggesting the title, to Kathleen Kiyuna for typing draft after draft, to Kenneth Saiki for editing, and to my husband Kiyoto for his translation of Japanese books, magazine articles and news clippings into English.

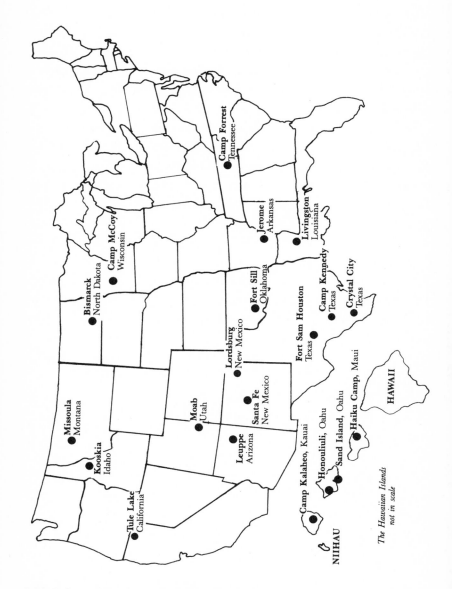

SITES OF HAWAI'I INTERNEE CAMP

INTRODUCTION

This is a true story of about 1,500 Hawai'i residents—Japanese aliens and American citizens—who were suddenly stripped of everything, including a name, to become an anonymous number. Bewildered, dumbfounded, they surrendered everything except the clothes on their back as they were incarcerated in flimsy tents behind barbed wire fences. They wondered, as they lived aimlessly day to day, what the future would bring.

The future brought 100 to over 1000 days of internment. It brought an examination of their past life and of their relationship with the country which they called home but which would not accept them because they were Asians. It brought an awakening and new awareness of self and priorities. Guarded by MPs with machine guns and trained dogs, they had to call upon whatever physical, mental, spiritual and intellectual strengths and skills they had to continue as rational human beings.

When bitterness and futility seemed to overcome them, they recalled the Japanese spirit of ganbare!—hold on! keep going! persevere!—which their parents and grandparents had shown. And as they hung on, they developed patience, compassion, and a new perspective on life.

The time is World War II (1941-1945). The facts are reconstructed from many interviews, diaries, books and articles written in Japanese and English, sketches and pictures. The internees still alive after forty years had learned to see their four years of internment in perspective, as part of their total lives in the country of their choice.

GANBARE! is a story of a group of people with unique experiences. To tell their story, they immersed their brushes into their own souls and translated the experiences into an example of the Japanese spirit. This is part of the heritage they are leaving us.

Patsy Sumie Saiki
March 12, 1983

CHAPTER 1

THE FISHERMEN:

Let's Go Home...

"Captain" Sutematsu Kida stared at the diamond-and-emerald-studded waves as he reluctantly steered his sampan toward Kewalo Basin near Waikīkī, but he didn't see them.

"How will the bombing of Pearl Harbor yesterday affect us Japanese alien fishermen?" he asked aloud, again and again. "We've been fishing off-shore for so many years now. Will the government keep us from going out?"

There was no answer. His son Kiichi and his helpers Kiho Uehara and Seiki Arakaki were too busy coiling the ropes and cleaning the fishing gear. They would be at Kewalo Basin in less than an hour and they wanted all equipment neatly stored away by the time they reached the landing.

Kida was worried. He and his crew—his son and the two others— had planned to fish for at least eight days, and here it was, only the fourth day—

Dec. 8, Monday—and they had to return to Kewalo Basin. He still had food, bait and fuel for another five days, and the 'ahi icebox was only half full. How could he pay expenses with an incomplete catch?

However, when he had come in offshore to lay anchor the night before, a sampan with a radio had slid alongside, the captain calling out, "Turn off your lights...turn off your lights..."

"Why?"

"There's a blackout!"

"Why?"

"Because Japan bombed Pearl Harbor!"

Bombed Pearl Harbor? Was Japan foolish enough to bomb American territory?

"Yes," Captain Onishi answered, as if he had read Kida's thoughts. "Japan bombed Pearl Harbor! We're at war with Japan!"

"At war!" All Kida could do was repeat what Captain Onishi was saying.

"The *Sumiyoshi Maru* and the *Shin-ei Maru* are here too, and we decided to wait until morning, then go back to Honolulu to see what's what. At a time like this, we should be with our families."

It was only after the *Myojin Maru* pulled away that Kida realized what could happen. He talked to his crew over a bowl of rice and a can of corned beef fried with onions. "I'm a Japanese alien, although I've lived here most of my life. I was told that as an alien, if there's a war with Japan, I wouldn't be able to fish offshore anymore. And if I can't fish, how do I support the family?"

"I can take the sampan out. I'm an American citizen," his son Kiichi said. Then he joked, "Seiki, Kiho, you'll have to call me 'Captain'."

"Kiichi, you're a hard worker but you're only 21. Seiki, you're only 21 too. Kiho, you're 29...at least more mature than the others. Do you think you have enough expertise?"

Fishing, if the objective was to catch fish for a livelihood and not as a pastime, consisted of both skills and art, just as writing a poem or shaping a ceramic pot was an art which required certain skills. A captain had to know more than how to lay the baskets, how to attach the lines with the many hooks, and what bait to use. A captain had to know the intricacies of flow of current, the direction and velocity of wind, the interplay of sun and clouds as they provided light and shadow in relationship to the depth of that ocean area, and the overall relationship of algae, small fish, larger fish, sun, sea, air and land. All was part of an art which required understanding of Nature and its many elements.

Kida looked at his slim, tanned son. Kiichi was especially precious to Kida because he was an only son among six daughters. Sure, he loved his daughters just as much, he told his wife, but it was Kiichi who would inherit Kida's boat, Kiichi who would have the responsibility of looking after his mother should anything happen to Kida. Fortunately, Kiichi was obedient and understanding. What other 21-year-old *nisei* would continue to be a commercial fisherman living off-shore for eight or more days on each fishing trip? There were only three others to talk to, limited space to walk on, no radio. Who else would cheerfully endure the blistering rays of Hawaiian sun on the ocean by day, and an uncomfortable pad at night? Who wouldn't prefer to be a house painter, a carpenter, a mechanic or an office boy? At home one could listen to music, go to the movies, date girls and eat decent food.

Christmas was coming. It was less than 20 days before Christmas, and how would he pay his bills for the food on board the sampan, the *kiawe* wood he used for fuel, the bait which would be useless for the next trip? He had counted on a full load of 'ahi, a fish which brought such good prices during the Christmas and New Year holidays! Kida twisted and turned on his pad after supper, until the exhaustion of the day numbed him and he too fell asleep off Māʻili Bay.

In the dawn's soft light which came late to Māʻili because of the mountains to the east, Kida saw the other sampans where they had dropped anchor. Soon Kiichi and Seiki made breakfast—coffee, pancakes and canned pear. Then, because they would not be fishing that day, they wore clean clothes, covering them with raincoats saturated with linseed oil to protect themselves from the spray and the occasional playful wave which would wash over them when they least expected it.

"Shall we leave now?" signalled Captain Sannosuke Onishi of the *Myojin Maru*. He led the other three sampans toward Kewalo Basin, and at first they moved as a group, but soon his sampan with a more powerful engine surged ahead, and Kida lost sight of him.

Captain Kida's *Kiho Maru* measured 12' by 48' and had been built like the fishing sampans used in Wakayama Prefecture in Japan, from where many of Hawai'i's fishermen had emigrated. Steering was done by a rod at one end of the boat; power was from the heat of a fire made with the slow-burning *kiawe* wood.

When Kida saw a P-40 approach, his mind was on the future. The plane he saw was the same as those he had seen so many, many times. The possible danger, the anger of the nation, the hatred of the sneak attack, were not real to him since all he knew at this point in time was that Pearl Harbor had been attacked. He hadn't questioned whether it had been one plane, two or twenty.

The plane with the red, white and blue insignia swooped low and strafed the sampan almost directly below it. Captain Kida arched backward for a split second, then fell over the steering rod. His son Kiichi and Kiho Uehara had not even turned to look at the plane, and were gunned in the back. Seiki Arakaki, hit on his left leg, was the only one who was able to crawl into the engine area and hide. The plane circled, attacked again from port, and, finally, a third time from the bow. The three dead men were riddled again and again, and Captain Kida's raincoat caught on fire, blackening his body until he seemed unrecognizable. But even in death, Kida's hands clenched the rudder, and his body, draped like a cloth puppet on the steering rod jammed extreme right, made the sampan spin round and around, round and around, in dizzying circles.

IDLE SAMPANS ON THE ALA WAI: Japanese fishermen who took their sampans out to fish following on Pearl Harbor were hit by American P-40 fire.

Photo Courtesy U.S. Army Signal Corps.

When the plane had left, Seiki crawled from the engine room and lowered his captain's body. Kiichi had moaned once, but the captain had not uttered a sound. Helplessly, Seiki wept to see the man who had been like a father to him, and his best friend Kiichi so still where a few minutes ago they had worked as a team. Only a few days earlier, Captain Kida had said, "Seiki, you can have any one of my unmarried daughters for your wife." Seiki had blushed, partly in happiness that his captain liked him so well.

Eventually a launch arrived to tow the sampan to Kewalo Basin. There Seiki Arakaki saw three bodies from another sampan being slipped into plastic bags. Then he was rushed to Queen's Hospital to have his leg wounds treated. When that was done, he was placed into a barricaded room, a room with wooden bars nailed over the windows and with two MPs guarding the single door.

Soon he was joined by a crew member of the *Shin-ei Maru*. "Captain Yokoyama and the other crew members—Ogawa and Okomi—were killed," he whispered dazedly. "And Okomi wasn't even a regular fisherman...he just agreed to help Yokoyama because the regular couldn't make it this trip."

So those were the three bodies Seiki Arakaki had seen being slipped into those plastic bags!

As Captain Onishi on the *Myojin Maru* rounded Barbers Point Naval Air Station, he saw at least four planes coming in his direction. When the planes neared, he was relieved to see they were P-40s, planes he had seen on practically every fishing trip during the past few years. "Our planes..." he said.

Suddenly one of the planes swooped low, and a hail of bullets whined, then clanged. One bullet punctured a fuel line and another, ricocheting off metal, punctured Captain Onishi's left arm.

"Hide...hide...some damn fool pilot thinks we're Japan boats," Onishi yelled. But hide where? The sampan was so small, there was no area four or even two people could crowd into for protection. "Take the raft..." He tried putting out a fire, ignoring the blood spurting from his arm.

But the plane had turned and was coming back. The men slipped into the water and made for the ropes dangling over the hull. The pilot strafed the sampan again, setting more fires, but missed the men hiding under the overhanging hull.

Stupefied and shocked, for all this had taken place in only a few minutes, the men hung on. A boat passed by but left without seeing them hiding with only their heads above water. Soon another boat—was it a Coast Guard cutter?—came, saw them, and dropped a ladder. Three of them climbed to safety, but the fourth, frozen in position, could not or would not touch the ladder.

"Don't worry. We'll use a smaller boat to pick him up. Tell him to hang on," an officer told Onishi. The crew members brought blankets because the three were shivering, and provided hot coffee and crackers. Medics applied first aid to Onishi's bullet wounds.

"Why didn't you fly an American flag? So we could identify your sampan?"

"American flag?" But they had been fishing offshore for more than 15 years without flying a flag!

"Can't you see the military is expecting a sea landing of Japan troops? We've been told to shoot first if there's any doubt..."

"We didn't know Japan was going to bomb Pearl Harbor. We were out fishing as usual, and didn't even have the radio on till last night."

"That's true. Have you taken food or oil to Japanese ships at sea? Or smuggled in any Japanese?"

Onishi was confused. On one hand, they were treating him and his crew kindly. He was, after all, a Hawai'i resident. But on the other hand they asked absurd questions; was it because he was a Japanese alien? He could only shake his head. He looked back at his *Myojin Maru*, being towed away, and saw even more fires had started on the deck. That was the last time he saw his sampan. Whether it burned, sank, or was confiscated, he was never to know. He didn't even have the opportunity to ask about the boat, for as soon as they reached Kewalo Basin, he was whisked to Queen's Hospital to have the bullet wound on his arm treated. Then he was led to the barricaded room where he saw one of Kida's crew, but not Kida.

A week later, when informed he was to be released from the hospital, he was overjoyed, but the car he was placed in drove in the opposite direction from his home. When the car stopped, he was at Iwilei Prison. There he was bombarded with questions.

"How many Japanese did you bring in to the island?"

"None." Clever! They didn't ask him, "Did you bring any Japanese to the island?"

"What about the oil you took to the ships at sea?"

"How can I carry oil in my small sampan? Besides, we never go beyond the two-mile limit."

After a few days he was told he could leave. "How do I go home?"

"That's up to you."

"May I make a phone call?" Neither his wife nor his young children could drive, so he called Detective Takeshi Nakafuji. The detective was flabbergasted.

"Onishi-san, what are you doing here? And what happened to you?"

"To tell you the truth, I don't know anything. Ask the MP."

"Do you know this man?" the MP asked.

"He's like a father to me," the detective answered. He escorted Onishi to his car and tenderly helped him in.

When Onishi's wife and children saw him, they burst into tears. His salt-encrusted clothes were filthy after two weeks of continuous wear. His face, with its scraggly beard, had a wild and lost look. His arm was heavily bandaged, and his feet were cracked and swollen after hours in salt water and exposure to cold cement floors for over two weeks. He had lost his slippers when he had jumped overboard that terror-filled morning.

The family rushed Onishi to the family doctor—Dr. Kazuo Miyamoto—only to find he had been interned on Dec. 7, 1941!

Captain Kenji Takumi of the *Sumiyoshi Maru* was more fortunate. Although the sampan was strafed, none were killed. Earlier, some bullets had plopped into the water around them, so Takumi had steered the sampan farther away from shore. Then, when a plane suddenly swerved low, Takumi and the others hid wherever there was protection of any kind or they could not be seen from above. When a Coast Guard cutter approached alongside, the men found Takumi with a bullet wound, but crew members Kichimatsu Urakami and Eiji Okimoto were safe. The fishermen were handed an American flag for identification and escorted to Kewalo Basin. From the pier, they were accompanied by MPs to Iwilei Prison. In a few days they were released.

It was Mrs. Kimie Shidaki, Captain Kida's eldest daughter, who was taken to Queen's Hospital to identify the bodies of her father, brother and friend. Her cousin, Katsukichi Kida, a fishing store proprietor, had been one of the first at the pier. He saw the blackened and bullet-riddled body of his uncle and immediately called his aunt to tell her of Captain Kida's death. Mrs. Kida was too numb with the loss of husband and only son to visit the morgue.

At the entrance to the makeshift room, a Hawaiian policeman gripped her shoulders comfortingly. "This isn't going to be easy," he warned. "It'll be a shock; you'll have to be strong." Kimie nodded. She was a priest's wife, and death was not a stranger to her. She had learned how to comfort others, and she knew how transient life was.

As she was about to enter, an MP stopped her. "Wait a minute, Jap. Do you have permission to enter?" The MP ignored the fact that the Hawaiian policeman was escorting her; he went personally to the desk to investigate. Then he motioned her brusquely into the room.

Bodies were stacked in every available space. When Kimie found her father's body, she noticed that his face and hands were clean although she had been told her father's body would be black and riddled with bullet holes. When she attempted to unbutton his shirt to see his wounds, an attendant warned, "No!"

"This is my father, Sutematsu Kida. This is my brother Kiichi. And this is our friend, Kiho Uehara," she said softly, as if afraid of waking the three lying there.

"Will you help us identify some of the other fishermen?"

"No, I can't...I can't." She felt faint, and the Hawaiian policeman assisted her outside to fresh air.

Her brother was also identified by the ID in his wallet; this was later returned to them. But her father's wallet, which held the money for salary and other expenses, was never found.

A week later, as they held prayer services before the Buddhist altar in their home, six men—two MPs, two policemen, and two in plain clothes—knocked at the door.

"Where is Sutematsu Kida?" one of the MPs asked. "We want to ask him a few questions."

"He's dead," Kimie answered bluntly. She pointed to a picture, draped in black, at the altar.

"Where's Kiichi Kida?"

"He's dead too." She pointed to another, a smaller picture.

"Do you know who killed them?"

"No, we don't." At a time like this, why say it was a P-40 pilot?

"Thank you." The MP made little checks on a clipboard he carried. He saw the flowers banked in the room, the lighted candles, the incense floating upward, the tears, the frightened neighbors who tried to hide their faces so they would not be identified. There was a regulation that no more than ten adults could assemble at any one time in any one place, and they were guilty of breaking this military rule.

But the MP did not disturb the group. Instead, he saluted the two men in the pictures, bowed to the bereaved family, and left. One Hawaiian policeman angrily kicked a tire of his car as he left.

CHAPTER 2

THE BACKGROUND:

Check, Checkmate!

The personal tragedies...the sudden deaths...that took place on the ocean had been repeated a thousand times over the day before. The fishermen, out of sight and sound of O'ahu, did not know this.

Actually, the prelude began many years earlier. Hawai'i, described by Mark Twain as "the loveliest fleet of islands anchored in any ocean," was wrested by a group of Americans from the Hawaiian Queen Lili'uokalani in 1894. After its annexation to the United States in July, 1898, the islands slowly became a bastion of military power with a fleet of carriers, battleships, cruisers, destroyers and submarines based at Pearl Harbor. There were army, air force or marine bases at Schofield Barracks, Hickam, Wheeler, Bellows, Kāne'ohe, Hale'iwa and 'Ewa.

The Japanese *issei* on Oahu believed implicitly in this might and were absolutely certain Japanese military forces, now rampaging in Manchuria and China, would not be foolish enough to take on the United States.

1940 was a big year for Japan, as it celebrated its 2,600[th] year of "known" existence under one line of emperors. As part of its festivities it awarded a certificate and a gift from the Emperor to those who had contributed substantially to the welfare of Japan or to the Japanese community in Hawai'i. Among the awardees were 27 from Hawai'i.

The list read like a Who's Who in Hawai'i's Japanese community in 1941.[1] Needless to say, they were interned during World War II, although for varying lengths of time, from a month for Rev. Chinpei Goto to four years for Editor Yasutaro Soga, Taichi Sato, Yukihide Kohatsu, Kango Kawasaki and many others.

Refusing the awards were the Rev. Takie Okumura of Makiki Christian Church and Editor Kinsaburo Makino of the *Hawai'i Hochi*, a Japanese-English daily. Rev. Okumura was said to have been instrumental in keeping Japanese Christian ministers from being interned, and Editor Makino had only a few of his staff interned, as compared to Editor Soga of the *Nippu Jiji* who had accepted a certificate.

July, 1941, was a busy month, beginning with July 5. The rumor was that assets of three Japanese banks would be frozen. Long lines queued from early morning to withdraw, within one day, about $300,000 from Sumitomo Bank and $40,000 each from Yokohama Specie Bank and Pacific Bank. But then people were informed that assets would not be frozen. After a few days of hesitation and probing, people again deposited their money. Later, without notice, the money was really frozen.

On July 31, the *Asama Maru* arrived from Japan with strandees who had been unable to return earlier. The *Asama* was scheduled to be the last of the ships to leave Japan, and on August 4, further sailings of passenger ships were suspended. However, in October, Nippon Yusen Kaisha's pride, the *Tatuta Maru*, sailed into Honolulu, and in November, only a month before the Pearl Harbor attack, the *Taiyo Maru* brought even more strandees back to the islands.

People ate their turkey on Thanksgiving and began preparing for the Christmas holidays. There was, on Dec. 7, 1941, a Japanese population of 159,534 in Hawai'i, which constituted 34.2 percent of the total population. Of these, 35,183 were *issei*. Some of them had been four or five years old when they had arrived in Hawai'i, and could not remember the country left behind. Nevertheless, because they were denied naturalization, they were Japanese citizens.

What the average person didn't know was that in March, 1941, a Japanese spy slipped into Honolulu. What happened was that in spring of 1941, Consul General Kiichi Gunji, a veteran diplomat who did not favor war with the United States, was replaced by genial Consul General Nagao Kita. Twelve days later, on March 26, 1941, Kita was joined by a minor consul who called himself Tadashi Morimura.

Most of the regular consulate work at that time was conducted by Consul Otojiro Okuda. Assisting him were two secretaries: Samon Tsukikawa, a code clerk, and Yokichi Seki, the senior secretary who was a civilian but who had spent a year in Japan's naval academy. He did most of the intelligence work.

Lesser staff members were Yasumasa Murata, a *kibei* clerk who clipped relevant news articles and gathered radio information to be sent to Japan; Masayuki "Dick" Kotoshirodo, another clerk; Johnny Mikami, a taxi driver but unofficially chauffeur for the Consulate; and three female servants.

There were of course Japanese intelligence officers working as espionage agents in major cities in the United States, just as any nation has agents in foreign countries. This was accepted diplomatically, and the United States knew who were in this country from Japan. But the agents were allowed freedom to circulate so that their actions could be observed and catalogued. Japan also knew that the United States knew most of its agents, so it trained a new man for Honolulu.

Born on March 7, 1914, this agent was only 27 when he arrived in Honolulu. A graduate of Etajima Naval Academy in 1933, he was a swimming champion and a fourth rank *kendo* student; he had taken torpedo, gunnery and aviation courses and had served as code officer on a cruiser. He was knowledgeable, with a good memory, and was comfortable in English. However, because of his heavy drinking and stomach problems, he had been retired temporarily from active duty and assigned to an office.

Then, in the spring of 1940, his superior approached him and asked if he would serve as a secret agent. Ensign Takeo Yoshikawa—that was his real name—agreed. At that point he was given the name Tadashi Morimura and a dossier was compiled. As Morimura he studied international law and English at Nippon University, passed his diplomatic exams, and was ready for his new position. Only in his drinking habits was Morimura still Yoshikawa.

At that time counter-espionage in Hawai'i was headed by Captain Irving H. Mayfield of the District Intelligence Office of the 14th Naval District; Major Byron M. Meurlott of the Criminal Investigation Division of Fort Shafter; Lt. Col. George W. Bicknell of the Hawaiian Department G2; Lt. Col. Edwin W. Raley of Hawaiian Air Force G2; and Special Agent Robert L. Shivers of the FBI Field Office. In addition, there were about a hundred officers and full-time investigators working under the command of these men.[2]

These agents compiled an "A," "B," and "C" list of Hawai'i Japanese who might prove disloyal in case of war between the United States and Japan. Those on the "A" list would be picked up immediately and confined; those on the "C" list would be kept under surveillance.[3]

The local agents watched the Japanese Consulate closely, since they knew this would be the chief source of information to Japan. In 1940, the District Intelligence Office of the 14th Naval District placed taps on six consulate business phones, plus a tap on the Consul General's residence phone. An average of about 60 calls per day was recorded, translated and circulated to the Hawai'i Department G2 office and to the FBI.[4]

At no time did Morimura make suspicious calls or ask questions regarding Pearl Harbor or air bases.

Captain Mayfield's office was not the only one to tap phones. Robert Shivers, FBI agent, had the office of Kenji Kimura, who served as general manager of Japan's gigantic shipping line, the Nippon Yusen Kaisha line, tapped. But a telephone company workman, doing other work in the basement of Dillingham Building, came across the tap and relayed this information to the telephone company who then reported this to the FBI and to Naval Intelligence.[5]

Mayfield, on being so informed, ordered the removal of taps from the Japanese Consulate, except for one left on the kitchen telephone. It was from this tap that the FBI learned that on Dec. 3, 1941, the consulate was burning papers. The FBI notified both Captain Mayfield and Lt. Col. Bicknell of the Hawaiian Department G2 of this fact. Bicknell is said to have reported this to General Walter C. Short, Commanding General, Hawaiian Army, while Mayfield did nothing with the information.[6]

On Nov. 1, 1941, the *Taiyo Maru* docked in Honolulu Harbor. The ship, instead of sailing directly to Hawai'i in its usual path, had followed a northern route before cutting sharply south. It was an unusual, roundabout way between two points, but the ship's captain did not question why he was requested to take this route, although privately he must have had some inkling.

Hawai'i's intelligence officers knew that there was a reason other than to return strandees from Japan for this ship to be sent to Hawai'i. They searched the passengers and baggage thoroughly, but could not discover anything.

Actually, four men serving as part of the ship's crew were officers of the Imperial Japanese Navy. One was Lt. Commander Suguru Suzuki and another was Lt. Commander Toshihide Maejima. The two were experts in air and surface ship operations; they noted velocity and direction of wind, pitch and roll of the ship, conditions in Hawai'i and in Pearl Harbor specifically, and the presence or absence of ships or planes encountered along the way.

The naval officers remained on ship, but were visited by Consul General Kita on several occasions, during which they handed him a list of 97 questions. Back at the Consulate, Yoshikawa compiled the answers to these questions, one of which was, "On what day of the week is there least activity in military installations?" The answer was, of course, "Sunday."

Returning to Japan on the *Taiyo Maru* were 238 alien Japanese and 210 American-Japanese, mostly minors being taken by their parents to a new home. Baggage was searched, papers inspected, and funds checked. There was tight security, but again nothing suspicious was uncovered.

The answers to the 97 questions, as well as hand-drawn maps, were compiled from information gathered by Yoshikawa during the previous eight months. He had gone on drives, sometimes with just the chauffeur, Johnny Mikami, and sometimes with a woman companion. Sometimes he sported a lei, and sometimes a cheap camera. He flew over Pearl Harbor on a sightseeing plane. He drank and ate at Shunchoro teahouse, later to be called Natsunoya, located high on a hill on 'Alewa Heights, overlooking Pearl Harbor. He drank at a bar on

College Walk, where sailors congregated. He even went to eat at Seaview Inn in Haleʻiwa, across the island from the Consulate, where a new air base had been established. He went on sightseeing trips to other islands in the Hawaiian chain.

Once he is said to have posed as a Filipino and became a dishwasher at a Pearl Harbor messhall. He even went swimming in the restricted Pearl Harbor waters to check whether there was a net at the Pearl Harbor entrance. He never carried pencil or paper; everything was photographed in his mind until he returned to his locked room. He sent about 150 messages to Japan. In spite of all this activity, no mention of him was made by the FBI or Naval Intelligence until much later.

On Nov. 26, 1941, when Admiral Isoroku Yamamoto and his flagship *Nagato* left for Hittokappu, in the mist-shrouded, rugged Kuriles a thousand miles north of Tokyo, Yamamoto's wide knowledge of Hawaiʻi and its waters and Yoshikawa's specific information on the number and placement of ships in port together promised a successful attack on Pearl Harbor for Japan.

Admiral Yamamoto—named Isoroku which means "56"—was born when his father was 56 years old. After graduating from Etajima Naval Academy in 1904, at age 20, he attended Harvard to learn aviation tactics, then served for two years at the Japanese Embassy in Washington, D.C. Because of his years in the United States, Yamamoto was keenly aware of the resources and strength the United States possessed, and of the American personality. He knew that although Americans seem apathetic or lethargic, they become united when the need arises.

Yamamoto was specific, systematic, and thorough. For example, he had studied Pearl Harbor and the Hawaiian Islands waters before the Pearl Harbor attack was ever considered, and had compiled a 500-page mimeographed book called *The Habits, Strengths, and Defenses of the American Fleet in the Hawaiian Area*. It contained information on the topography of the islands, on Hawai'i's reefs, on military and naval installations, and on patterns of U.S. air patrols and ship movements. He had accumulated detailed information on many other strategic naval areas.

By 1941, he had risen from captain to rear admiral and was Vice-Minister of the Navy Ministry. When he urged caution to the chiefs of staff over involvement with the U.S., the warlords, drunk with power over victories in Manchuria and China, laughed him off. To prevent Admiral Yamamoto's assassination which he suspected was being plotted, Navy Minister Mitsumasa Yonai, his direct superior, named him Commander-in-Chief of the Combined Fleet, with headquarters on the flagship *Akagi*. This at least kept Yamamoto safe from assassins on land.

When Yamamoto realized his attempts to keep Japan from becoming involved in a war with U.S. were fruitless, he determined that some strategy would have to be devised to make the U.S. defenseless for a period of time. During that interim of weakness, Japan would have the opportunity to forge ahead in southeast Asia and build her defenses. As he told his trusted friend, Rear Admiral Ryunosuke Kusaka, "If we are ordered to fight the United States, we might be able to score a runaway victory and hold our own for six months or a year. But in the second year the Americans will increase their strength, and it will be very difficult for us to fight on with any prospect of final victory."[7]

With this in mind he plotted a surprise attack on Pearl Harbor to render the carriers and battleships temporarily useless. His plan was heavily influenced by the fact that the Japanese Navy had destroyed the Russians' Pacific Squadron in 1905 at the Battle of Japan Sea. Yamamoto himself had been on Admiral Heihachiro Togo's flagship in that attack, when the Japanese fleet had destroyed Russia's seven battleships and five cruisers. Admiral Togo, commander of that 1905 fleet, was Admiral Yamamoto's idol, and Yamamoto wanted to use the same strategy for which Japan had been censured once by the world: attack on a nation without first declaring war.

He selected Vice-Admiral Chuichi Nagumo, Commander-in-Chief of Japan's First Air Fleet, as leader of the strike force, assisted by Rear Admiral Ryunosuke Kusaka. Charged with implementation of the details as well as of planning was Deputy Chief of Staff Minoru Genda, who in turn selected his classmate Mitsuo Fuchida to coordinate and lead the attack. All five trusted each other's abilities, intelligence and integrity. They complemented each other in personality, so that one would recognize the strong points of a plan while another would see all the pitfalls.

The team planned two waves of attack. The first, commanded by Fuchida, would have Lt. Commander Shigeharu Murata in charge of 40 Nakajima-97 torpedo bomber planes, Lt. Commander Kakuichi Takahashi of 51 Aichi dive-bombers with 500-lb bombs, and Lt. Commander Shigeru Itaya with 43 Mitsubishi Zero fighters. The second wave, led by Lt. Commander Shigekazu Shimazaki, would have about 170 planes. In all, there were 320 planes; 304 would participate in the attack, and the rest would be on their ships should an American attack come from the air.

To prepare for the attack, which he named "Operation Z" after Admiral Togo's "Z" signal at Tsushima, Yamamoto moved some of his ships to southern Kyushu for special exercises. He had his planes fly in from the north over Shiro, a ridge of mountains, follow winding Iwasaki Valley, release dummy bombs and torpedoes while skimming over the bay, then swiftly return toward the mountains. The men practiced vertical drops, discharging loads from 1,500 feet. Only Yamamoto knew from his years of study that the terrain and atmospheric conditions of that locale were similar to the course the pilots would take over the island of O'ahu on their way to Pearl Harbor.

Moving secretly and independently, six carriers, two battleships, three cruisers, nine destroyers and other supply ships moved into Hittokappu Bay. Etorofu Island had a large deep bay; the village had only three dwellings, a small concrete pier, a post office and telegraph facilities. Once the ships had congregated in the harbor, the gunboat *Kunajiro* impounded outgoing mail and telegrams, and patrol boats prevented fishermen from leaving land. The ships then moved together on Nov. 27 to its designated area 200 miles north of O'ahu.

Early in the morning of Dec. 7, Sunday, Vice Admiral Nagumo moved about his ship restlessly. In a few hours the planes would be on their way. Were the Americans secretly waiting for them, lulling them with soft Hawaiian music on the radio? Had they been discovered, for how could Yamamoto or anyone else be so successful as to move ships, men and supplies without someone guessing as to what had been planned? What if the Japanese navy itself commented on the disappearance of 30,000-ton aircraft carriers *Akagi* and *Kaga*, or the 18,000-ton *Soryu*, *Hiryu*, *Shokaku* and *Zuikaku*? How could the battleships *Hiei* and *Kirishima*, the cruisers *Tone*, *Chikuma* and *Abukuma*, plus nine destroyers, three large subs, eight tankers and about 360 planes remain unreported without expressed surmises which could be picked up by Americans even if mentioned in code?

The ships had been needed elsewhere in the Pacific. Were the Imperial Navy commanders making best use of their ships and planes?

Tension twisted Nagumo's stomach, but then he remembered calm and capable Commander Mitsuo Fuchida and the other pilots who had been carefully selected and precisely trained. Nagumo and Genda had done all they could. Now he must relax, so that his confidence would be communicated to those who would be going out in a few hours, some never to return.

Nagumo would have been even more disturbed had he known that not a single carrier was berthed at Pearl Harbor that morning. Vice-Admiral William F. Halsey, Jr. was on his way to Wake Island with the aircraft carrier *Enterprise*, three heavy cruisers and nine destroyers. Rear Admiral John Henry Newton was on his way to Midway with the *Lexington*, three cruisers and five destroyers. The carrier *Saratoga* was in San Diego. Nagumo's targets would have to be the battleships *California*, *Maryland*, *Oklahoma*, *Tennessee*, *West Virginia*, *Arizona*, *Nevada* and the *Pennsylvania*, in drydock.

At 7:30 a.m., Dec. 7, the two highest military officers in Hawai'i were preparing for a scheduled game of golf. Even Lt. General Walter C. Short, commanding the Hawaiian Department of the Army, is said to have interpreted the heavy bombing in the islands as another large and very realistic Navy battle practice.

Admiral Husband E. Kimmel, commanding the Pacific fleet, had received a call earlier that morning reporting that an unidentified submarine had been depth-bombed, but he had asked for verification and amplification since similar reports had been received several times before.

Actually, it was as early as 3:59 a.m. that the *Ward*, on patrol outside Pearl Harbor, had received a signal from the minesweeper *Condor* that a strange object had been sighted, an object that trailed after the ship, much as a tin can trails after a wedding car when seen from some distance. The *Ward*'s commander, a Lt. William W. Outerbridge, searched for it. At 6:45 a.m. he found it and scored a hit. A Navy patrol plane then depth-bombed it. After all, no American sub would have traveled submerged so close to the Pearl Harbor entrance. Months later the mini-sub was dredged from outside the harbor, the remains of its two occupants still in it.

On the same morning, in a remote spot in the Ko'olau Range on the northern end of O'ahu, a radar installation manned by two privates—Joseph Lockard and George Elliott—showed a large blip on the radar screen. It indicated that many planes, perhaps more than fifty, were converging on O'ahu. Lockard and Elliott excitedly reported this unusual occurrence to a lieutenant, but that officer did not share their urgency for he was expecting 12 U.S. Army Air Corps B-17s which were to be refueled in Hawai'i; the pilots were to rest before proceeding to the Philippines. Had this flight not been expected at about the same time the Japanese planes were zooming toward O'ahu, the bases might have been alerted and thousands of lives saved.

By 9:45 a.m. Pearl Harbor and many air fields were in ruins. 2008 Navy men and officers were killed; the battleship *Arizona* alone had buried 1102 men. The Army lost 218 men, the Marines 109. The wounded numbered over 700 Navy, 364 Army and 69 Marines. The lethargy and complacency of the people had disappeared, and anger and fear were the dominant emotions.

A little later that morning, 72-year-old Governor Joseph E. Poindex-ter read a Proclamation of Emergency over the radio. General Walter C. Short had pointed out to him that more planes could be attacking Hawai'i that night and that a landing by Japanese troops was possible. There was also the danger of saboteurs from among the local Japanese residents. Hawai'i needed—must have—martial law. Poindexter reluctantly agreed. Martial law in Hawai'i lasted a long three years, until October, 1944.

With martial law was suspended the writ of habeas corpus and expected Constitutional guarantees. The courts were to close the next day, and when they reopened on Dec. 16, 1941, they were under the jurisdiction of the military governor, although some jury trials were later allowed.

All through the day on Dec. 7, fires burned on different plantations. Anti-aircraft strafing could be heard, but human nature being what it is, many housewives were busy with their own self-survival tactics. Mindful of their children and scarcities in past years, they rushed to whatever stores were open, stocking up on powdered milk, flour, rice, sugar, salt, coffee and toilet tissue. In a few days stores were ordered closed for an inventory of food and other supplies in the islands. Store owners were warned they were to sell to the general public, not only to their friends. Residents were urged to buy only what they needed because of the scarcity of certain items. This of course spurred hoarders to stock up even more.

The fires raging in the cane fields and an Iwilei gas tank fire cast a glow in the sky that night. But the rest of Oʻahu was dark, for General Short had ordered a blackout from 6 p.m. to 6 a.m. which was later adjusted to "sunset to sunrise." A dim-out was not permitted until July, 1942, and complete blackout regulations were not lifted until July, 1944.

The men at the military bases on the evening of Dec. 7 were jittery. Any plane could be an enemy plane. Any boat could be an enemy boat attempting to infiltrate military bases. In that fear-laden atmosphere, six planes from Admiral Halsey's carrier *Enterprise*, returning from a fruitless search for Admiral Nagumo's carriers, were told to land at Ford Island instead of returning to their ship. The guns at Pearl Harbor raked the planes with antiaircraft fire. Of the six, four were destroyed, and one damaged. The tears shed that night were anguished as well as angry ones.

In these fear-laden hours, 13 squads comprised of members from Army Intelligence, FBI and police began knocking on doors. The authority for action against those picked up, chiefly *issei* but with a handful of *nisei*, was in Section 21, Title 50, U.S. Code, first enacted July 6, 1798 and amended April 16, 1918.[8]

The U.S. Supreme Court had interpreted that war gives the "sovereign" full right to take into custody persons who were considered "alien enemies" and to confiscate their property.[9]

Also, an alien enemy arrested under Section 21, Title 50, could not claim he was deprived of his liberty without the usual due process of law; the Presidential warrant on which the arrest was made did not need to disclose the grounds on which the alien was taken into custody.[10]

It was also held that the President's action in summary arrest and detention of an alien enemy under this Section was conclusive and not subject to review on *habeas corpus*.

On Dec. 7, 1941, President Roosevelt issued Proclamation 2525 under the authority granted by Sec. 21, Title 50, U.S. Code. The Secretary of War was given the responsibility regarding the conduct of alien enemies in Hawai'i. So on Dec. 7, 1941, martial law was declared, and beginning that day, the FBI began taking into custody the Japanese alien enemies it considered dangerous and turned them over to the Immigration and Naturalization Service. By the evening of Dec. 8, 1941, 345 Japanese in Hawai'i and 867 on the Mainland U.S. had been picked up.[11]

By October, 1943, 14,807 alien enemies had been taken into custody. Of these, 5,303 were Japanese, 5,977 were Germans and 3,503 were Italians. There were also 24 Hungarians, Rumanians and Bulgarians.[12]

Executive Order 9066, signed by President Roosevelt on February 19, 1942, which was to cause so much suffering to the West Coast Japanese, was still two months in the future.

CHAPTER 3

IMMIGRATION OFFICE:

What's Your Name, Furuya?

"Prisoners," the driver said, tapping his identification badge wearily and waiting for the gate to open. He had made this trip four times today and he hated to see the faces of the men—especially of the invalids and of the elderly—as they were picked up. But he was only a driver and went where he was told to go.

The car stopped at the front door of the darkened Immigration Office in Honolulu near a pier. Only when the heavy door was opened could the "prisoners" see a thin shaft of light from behind another door.

Yasutaro Soga and others were taken into a reception room where six MPs registered them. Name? Address? Telephone number? Occupation?

The information was already on an interrogator's sheet. These simple questions, they were told later, were to verify that they had the right person. Despite such thoroughness, however, mistakes still occurred. A priest on the FBI list had moved out of a rented house and another tenant had just moved in. It took a week before the FBI was satisfied that the agitated man was indeed not the priest whose name was on its list.

After the questions, an MP did a body search. Everything—wallet, keys, watch, pen, cigarettes, lighter—except handkerchief and glasses was taken and deposited in a manila envelope with the owner's name scribbled on it.

"Upstairs!"

Upstairs? Were there bedrooms upstairs?

They groped their way up in the darkness, using a railing and an MP's flashlight's beam for direction. A guard at the top of the stairs unlocked a door, pushed the men in, then relocked the door. All night it was open, push bodies in, and relock the door!

After Yasutaro Soga's eyes adjusted to the darkness, he saw many tiers of three iron shelf-beds with thin mattresses lining the walls. Mattresses were also all over the floor, with two or three men on each. The room was stuffy. Although built for about 75, it held double that number.

Someone took Soga's hand and directed him to a corner. "There's space here..."

"Thank you..." His ordinarily soft voice sounded loud in the muted room.

"Soga, is that you?" Soga recognized Dr. Mori's voice.

"Mori, are you here already?"

"I'm here too, Soga-san," another voice called out. It was 84-year-old hotelman Komeya, who had been ill and in bed for the past two years. Soga shook his head in disbelief. Why would anyone intern an aged invalid?

Someone near him whispered, "Bishop Gikyo Kuchiba, Dr. Tokue Takahashi, Rev. Ryuten Kashiwa, Rev. Buntetsu Miyamoto and Yugoro

Kusao were picked up early and they came handcuffed! Like criminals!"

Handcuffed? A physician whose skills even the white community respected highly? A bishop? Soga was glad he had been picked up at about 8 p.m., after the first wave of hysteria and chaos had passed.

Someone managed to open the rusty window and let fresh air flow in. "The moon is so clear and bright," he observed with wonder, as if it were the first time he had seen a moon. Somehow, even that innocent remark triggered fear.

"If the Japan planes come back, there's no escape for us. We're locked in, and we're so close to the piers."

In the morning, each person picked up a mess kit with a cup of coffee and two slices of bread with jam. When he was through eating he returned the tray, then was allowed to walk outside.

When the whistle blew, he had to single-file back to the room upstairs.

After breakfast began interrogations. Newspaperman Shoichi Asami was first to be called. When he returned, the others crowded around him and asked, "What did they say? What did they want to know?"

"They know all about you," he answered. "Not only when and where you were born, but how many times you've gone to Japan, when you went and when you returned. They know who your relatives in Japan are. Dr. Takahashi, they know your brother is vice-admiral in the Japanese navy and that you like to sail on your yacht on Sundays. They asked me if you went out to meet representatives of your vice-admiral brother. They have a record of events I forgot long ago." He shook his head in wonder at their thoroughness, not realizing that a record of all such activities would be on file at the Japanese Consulate.

"But I learned something new," he said. "They captured a Japan officer. A naval officer."

"A Japan naval officer? Did the Japanese navy land on O'ahu?"

"I don't know. Evidently there was only one officer. I heard them talking about it. Strange, isn't it? To have only one?"

"How many people were killed in yesterday's bombing?"

"That I wouldn't know. I doubt if even those at home know. That kind of news won't be released for a while."

At 3 p.m. lunch was served. This time there was some corned beef with the two slices of bread and coffee. As they stood eating under the eaves of the building, someone noticed a young Japanese carpenter stringing barbed wire atop the 10-foot wall.

"Look! A carpenter! He's Japanese!" they whispered. "Maybe he could give a message to one of our families."

They edged closer to the wall and spoke loudly. I'm Kumaji Furuya from Gulick Avenue. I know my wife would be so relieved if someone informed her I'm here. What's your name" he asked Obata.

"I'm Soichi Obata from Kaimukī Avenue."

"And I'm Hego Fuchino from Kaloko Lane," volunteered Fuchino. And on and on it went. Did the young carpenter understand Japanese? So few *nisei* did. Would he remember at least one name and address, and would he call, looking up the number in the telephone book? They repeated their names over and over again, until the whistle blew and they had to march inside. They stared at the carpenter, pleading that he have eye contact with one of them. "Look at us, please look at us. Aren't your parents from Japan too? Can't you do this favor for us? Let our wives know we are alive and well? Haven't Japanese always helped one another in emergencies, in time of need?" But the carpenter kept his eyes on his work.

That evening and again the next day, they looked for the carpenter, but the barbed wire was up—three parallel rows pointing inward to deter anyone who could climb up ten feet of smooth wall.

Lying on the mattress in their one suit of clothes, they wondered what would happen to them. Furuya was sure he at least would be released once a thorough investigation had been made. After all, he had done nothing, absolutely nothing, that would warrant his being held a prisoner. The others—who knew? But he knew himself, and he knew he had been a good resident of this country…for how long? Was it thirty, forty years?

Yasutaro Soga, editor of the *Nippu Jiji*, one of the two Japanese language newspaper dailies in Honolulu in 1941, had lived in the islands 42 years. He had arrived as a student when 25, on Dec. 31, 1899. The *Hongkong Maru* had carried 628 others. This was a popular year for immigration from Japan to Hawai'i, and a total of 3,725 had arrived in December alone. The total for the year 1899 was a huge 25,499. These men were welcomed, as sugar plantations needed more and more workers. Hawai'i was no longer a royal kingdom; it had been annexed to the United States, and plantations were expanding.

The evening of Dec. 7, a car with blackout lights had eased to a quiet stop at his home in Kaimukī, and two armed guards had knocked at the door. They had asked that he come with them for interrogation at the Immigration Station. His wife had quickly slipped him a vest and coat plus three handkerchiefs. Soga himself had picked up three song books. As his grandchildren Walter and Helen and daughter-in-law Miya watched, Soga was escorted to the front gate and into the car.

"Don't catch cold," his wife had whispered. He wanted to reply, to say something, anything. "Take care of the children," "I'll be home soon," or "I love you all." But the words had stuck in his throat and his voice had been inaudible except to himself, and the small wave he gave was all the affection he could share with his family that night.

On the other side of the city, in Kalihi, Kumaji Furuya heard the knock on the front door. He knew it would be the FBI, but he was so sure he would return that same night that he intended going in his shirt.

His wife, however, insisted that he take a coat. When he went into his bedroom and pulled open the top dresser drawer, he felt cold steel at his back. The MP withdrew the handgun when he saw the drawer held handkerchiefs and socks.

Already in the car were Insuranceman George Otani, Rev. Jyoei Oi, Contractor Gosuke Shigemoto and Rev. Shigezo Shimoda. "The 'O's' and 'S's'," he said. "How come I'm here? I'm F."

"Shut up. No talking," the MP warned.

At the gate to the Immigration Station, the sentry required identification, and the driver's weary answer was, "We're bringing in more prisoners."

Matsujiro Otani of Mānoa had been up early on Dec. 7. For the past three days he had hosted a grand festival to celebrate the opening of Otani Market at 'A'ala Park. The area he had developed had space for many shops and already most of them had been rented. A mountain of 100-pound bags of rice lay piled in the market, with names of contributors who were wishing him good-luck. Dozens upon dozens of bouquets of flowers added color and fragrance to the festive occasion.

Sunday was the day Otani had reserved to thank the many workers who had made the past three days a success. So he bustled around, despite poor health, impervious to strange and alarming sounds: a series of explosions, fire trucks screaming, planes buzzing and shrapnel whining. Some of the employees and guests said they thought the bombing was real, while others believed it was practice as usual, with radio stations participating to provide more realism.

About 11 a.m., however, Governor Joseph Poindexter himself shakily announced on Radio Station KGU that Japan had bombed Pearl Harbor. A radio announcer then requested that those with trucks report to Pearl Harbor or Schofield Barracks to help transport the wounded to hospitals. Otani immediately dispatched two trucks, but being that the drivers had Japanese faces, the trucks were turned away at the gate to Pearl Harbor. The drivers then drove to the army base at Schofield Barracks, but again were turned away.

Otani closed up shop at 4 p.m. and made his way home, wondering what the future would bring. Before he could take a hot bath to dissolve the day's exhaustion from his bones, there was a knock at the door.

The MP refused him time to change his clothes or to wear his shoes, but his wife threw his shoes into the car where Uyemon Inokuchi, the principal of Mānoa Japanese Language School, waited quietly.

"Who are the other prisoners we are to pick up?" the driver asked one of the guards. That was when Matsujiro Otani realized he was to be a prisoner of his adopted country.

At the Japanese Hospital, which had been established following a bubonic plague and a disastrous several-block fire in 1900, Dr. Kazuo Miyamoto was making his usual morning rounds before proceeding to his office. He saw black smoke and what sounded like aerial bombardment, but since Hawai'i had been in the midst of "war maneuvers" the past few weeks, he merely marveled at the authenticity of the "attack." It sounded almost real!

Curious, he climbed to the roof of the hospital to see what was happening. Two planes came zooming away from the ocean and headed for the hills. Their "sun" insignia was clearly visible. The radio had kept repeating it was a real air raid; finally Dr. Miyamoto believed the announcer.

He had seven patients in the hospital. "I want all my patients released, except the one with pneumonia," he ordered. "At a time like this, it's better for a family to be together. Both patients and relatives will be less anxious." As he hastened to wind up his round of visits, he heard his name. He was being paged…he was to report for duty at Fort Shafter!

He and several other general practitioners reported to administer first aid to military personnel. There were so many wounded, the injured were placed on mattresses without any sheets. The clean sheets were being torn for use as bandages.

Only a few days before, Dr. Miyamoto and some other physicians had attended a seminar conducted by an eminent New York medical professor who had said that in an emergency, one could use soap and water to irrigate wounds. They had all laughed, thinking of their equipment and shelves of drugs. But already they were having to put the professor's advice to use, for medical supplies were limited.

More serious cases were sent to operating rooms. "I don't need to go. Send him, he's in greater need..." the injured insisted. Dr. Miyamoto was impressed. He had thought young people rather selfish and shallow, with their focus on dance, music and sex. But in an emergency they were men, considerate of the welfare of others and willing to make sacrifices that could mean life or death for themselves.

"Damn Germans!" one of the wounded cursed.

"Germans? Those were Jap planes," his neighbor corrected him. "Didn't you see the sun insignia on the planes?"

"Oh, sure, they were Jap planes, but Japan couldn't plan anything with such precision. It had to be the damn German pilots. The Japs only carried out the plans."

Dr. Miyamoto worked steadily until 1 p.m., then was told he could go home. "Can you come again tonight?" he was asked. He nodded and left.

Some premonition, however, told him to be ready for any other circumstance. He therefore stopped at his office on Kukui Street and took his valuables, including his bank book, home to his wife. On the way to the car he saw, near a noodle shop, a telephone post with a piece of flesh still caught on a nail—too high to be reached by anyone without a ladder. The reality of the bombing and shelling of the island hit him more forcefully than all the injured he had been treating all day. Some innocent resident, happy that it was Sunday, a day of rest, had gone out for a morning walk, curious as to the drone of planes and staccato explosions. Now he was a casualty, a name on a list, instead of a family member sitting across the kitchen table. Dr. Miyamoto drove home to wash the smell of dead and dying that enveloped him physically and spiritually.

Later, instead of the expected call from the Medical Corps, there was a knock at the door.

"Dr. Kazuo Miyamoto? We would like to ask you some questions. Please come with us." The MPs waited politely as Dr. Miyamoto went to get his coat.

"Please cancel tomorrow's appointments," he called to his wife as he left, sandwiched between two husky MPs. He was realistic enough to know that this was a game of war.

That night, the four—Soga, Furuya, Otani and Miyamoto—slept in the one overcrowded room, each wondering why he had been selected by the FBI, although from his activity in the Japanese community, it might have been inevitable. War was a serious game played by antagonists who needed every advantage on its side. The four—or the 175 in the large room—were not there because they were disloyal but because they could be disloyal if the circumstances demanded it. So must have thought the intelligence officers and they were not taking any chances that they could be wrong!

CHAPTER 4

SAND ISLAND:

A Spoon is Missing. Strip!

On Tuesday, Dec. 9, two days after the Pearl Harbor bombing, one half of the group in the Immigration Office were told to line up outside. Each section couldn't decide which was better, to be in the first group or in the second. The second group was handed mops and brooms and told to clean up the large room and the toilets.

The first group lined up in rows and boarded trucks waiting for them. In each truck were three bayoneted soldiers to guard them. The trucks proceeded to a pier a short distance away. There the men were told to board a barge.

"This is a pineapple barge," Kumaji Furuya whispered. "I can even smell the pineapple. This means we're going to be taken to Moloka'i. I heard a rumor that in case of war, we Japanese would be held prisoners on Moloka'i."

But within a few minutes, they reached land. "Out!" was the order. "And hurry up."

Why, this was Sand Island, that deserted island next to the entrance of Honolulu Harbor. In 1869, when smallpox was discovered on a ship entering the harbor, the Hawaiian rulers realized a quarantine station or hospital was needed. They built a lighthouse and a hospital on the island and called the place Kahaolao. With the addition of coral dredged from Honolulu Harbor, the island measured ten acres by 1898. Eventually the military gained control of the island, and about five acres were fenced in to accommodate military personnel. Now, why were they on Sand Island?

Two abreast, the men were marched into a *kiawe* thicket. Was this a death march? Were they going to be shot without even a trial?

But then they reached a large Spanish-type building; its windows were covered with black paper.

"Strip!" was the next order.

Why? Did Hawai'i have a gas chamber? But this was America. Wasn't someone, anyone, going to protest? That although they were not American citizens, they were permanent residents and as such entitled to some sort of trial to attest to their innocence or guilt of whatever charge was being filed against them?

The MPs examined them and their clothes, then ordered them to dress. But before they resumed their walk, an officer spoke to them.

"I am Captain John G. Coughlin," the 6'5", ramrod straight officer said. "You are not criminals. But you are enemy nationals. Your treatment here will depend upon your behavior. For some years I have been interested in your people and your culture. I think I know you. After the other day, I know we have a worthy opponent in you people. We will respect you as an individual, but since you are all prisoners of war, you must follow rules and regulations. You will all be treated equally and fairly!"

Relieved, they resumed their walk and soon came to a tile building which housed hot and cold showers, latrines, and a kitchen. On the way they discussed what Coughlin had said.

"We'll be treated equally..." This was food for thought. The concept of equality was accepted theoretically but realistically ? In the immediate past they had been respected bishops and priests, school teachers and principals, newspaper editors and reporters, bank managers and corporation presidents. The aura of eminence and esteem had surrounded them by virtue of their title, their position. Now all were to be treated equally... president and laborer, bishop and fisherman.

To the young soldier fresh from the Mainland, the Japanese men all looked alike. So it was to be a new role for many of the internees, not having others run to do their bidding. It was an alien environment, where actions would count more than words or title. The "man" was now separated from the "title."

This fact was immediately thrust upon them. "Pick up a tent and set it up. Four of you will sleep in one tent so get into groups and work cooperatively."

It was getting dark; a light rain fell and a chilly ocean breeze penetrated their clothes. Four priests or four educators who automatically tended to group together through past friendship struggled with the tents, looking at others to see what would be the first step. Usually bishops and business executives had others to do such manual labor.

Some of the men were shedding tears of frustration when the fishermen and contractors came to their rescue. Soon all the tents were up.

"Pick up a cot and set it up." Many parents had seen their eight- or nine-year-olds assemble cots in back yards, but setting up even a cot was difficult for some of the elderly. It was about 9 p.m. when, wet with perspiration and rain, they finally completed setting up the cots. At about that time the other half of the "prisoners" came marching in, carrying the 84-year-old Komeya who had collapsed. Quickly someone gave him his cot and tried to make him comfortable. Others went to help set up tents and cots for the new contingent.

Each person received two blankets, a pillow, and some sandwiches. Although wet and dirty, they fell asleep from sheer exhaustion. This was to be Day 3 of the war in the Pacific Theater and Day 1 at Sand Island.

The next morning, they saw that the tents had been haphazardly set up, so under the leadership and direction of Architect Hego Fuchino and some contractors, they dismantled, then realigned the tents. The guards were impressed with their initiative, capability and artistry, and complimented them.

Capt. Coughlin set forth certain rules and regulations, but gave the men conditional self-rule. One hundred and sixty internees were to be divided into four groups of 40 men each. Then each sub-group was again to be divided into groups of ten. The responsibility of each group and sub-group leader was to assist in settling problems and to communicate his group's concerns to his immediate superior. The head of the 160 men was to coordinate all efforts and communicate with military leaders.

Because he could speak English, Genji Otani appointed himself spokesman or leader and assumed the title of "Admiral." Henceforth, successive spokesmen were called "Admiral" on Sand Island.

Heading sub-groups of 40 internees each were Yoshinobu Sasaki, principal of Makiki Japanese Language School; Kensaku Tsunoda, administrator at Japanese Hospital on Kuakini Street; Kenji Kimura, of the Japan shipping giant Nippon Yusen Kaisha; and Harry Shiramizu, a reporter for the newspaper *Nippu Jiji*.

Things worked out well when, three days later, on Dec. 12, command was transferred to a Captain Carl F. Eifler from Schofield Barracks. Eifler had been a California policeman, a reserve officer, and an inspector at the California-Mexico border. Physically, Eifler struck fear in the internees just with his looks. Over six feet, weighing 280 pounds of bone and muscle, he had a 55" chest and a 42" waist.

SAND ISLAND: Elderly Internees were unaccustomed to manual labor and had to depend upon others to help them set up their tents in neat rows. Below: Internees who had ample spare time on their hands sometimes decorated the tents in which they were housed.

Photos Courtesy U.S. Army Signal Corps.

On Dec. 7, Sunday, Reserve Officer Eifler had an assignment to report to Schofield Barracks for a routine 24-hour duty beginning at 11 a.m. Awakened at 7:55 a.m. by his staff sergeant Vincent Curl who reported that "red planes were bombing Wheeler Air Field,"[1] Eifler answered that it must be practice as usual. But he dressed and made his way to Schofield, usually a 45-minute drive from his home but today a madhouse of concrete ribbon with traffic speeding both ways! He did not know that he would have to be on his feet for the next 90 hours!

On Dec. 12, while on duty at Fort Shafter, Eifler saw his provost marshal and a guard with a sawed-off shotgun approach him. The provost marshal ordered Eifler to accompany them.

The first thought that ran through Eifler's mind, he said later, was, "Is my German ancestry going to get me interned? The way the Germans were interned during World War I?"

He asked, "Will I be returning soon, sir, or shall I turn over my company to my lieutenant?"

"Turn over your command to your lieutenant," he was instructed.

With a sinking feeling, he realized he would not be returning to Ft. Shafter. But, head high, he got into the car with Honolulu Police Chief Gabrielson on one side of him and the provost marshal on the other. The guard with the shotgun sat in front with the driver.

Soon the car reached the Police Station and Chief Gabrielson got out. "Be seeing you, Carl," he said with a wave of his hand. Eifler took his first deep breath. He was not going to be interned, after all.

The car then proceeded to the Customs House, where Eifler was Chief Inspector.

"Carl, we want you released from Customs to take active command of Sand Island," he was told.

"The internment camp?"

"No, the detainment camp. Your company will be the 111th Military Police Company."

"And my men, sir?"

"The men in Company K are needed where they are. You will have to start from scratch."

"In that case, sir, I have two requests. First, I would like to keep my staff sergeant, Vincent Curl. Second, I would like to pick my own men. To get them, I would like to borrow three trucks."

The requests were granted. His next act was to drive through the streets of Honolulu. When he saw a well-coordinated, able-bodied man, he talked to him about joining the Army now. He also collected men from the University of Hawai'i and from the National Guard. In all, he picked up 240 men.

The puzzled youth were then ordered to do calisthenics. As the hours went by, one after another fell from sheer exhaustion, until finally only 60 men were left on their feet. The others were excused to return home.

The 60 were then ordered to run a quarter mile. The first one returning was named senior sergeant; the others received rank accordingly.

"How many of you can aim and fire a gun?" The answer was "None."

"All right. We'll begin right now." He divided the men into small teams, set up some targets and began his instruction. He insisted upon practice, practice, practice.

A week later, the group, now part of the 811th Military Police Company, was brought to full strength. Most of the men were from the local National Guard.

In the beginning there were no rules at Sand Island. The island had originally belonged to and was a branch of Immigration and Naturalization Services, the "Quarantine Station Branch," with a crematorium on the grounds. There were several small buildings and a large 14-room building where Eifler established his headquarters in one of the rooms.

Because of the lack of rules regarding civilian internees, Eifler drew up his own. No one knew when an invasion by sea or air was immi-

Carl F. Eifler commanded Sand Island Camp during the first three months following the Pearl Harbor attack.

Photo Courtesy U.S. Army (Ret.) Col. Carl F. Eifler.

nent, so he required strict adherence to schedules and rules. For his men, he insisted on firmness, fairness, control over the situation, and no fraternization between guard and detainee. His men could engage in sports, attend movies, and receive one overnight pass per month.

Where Capt. Coughlin had been too busy during his three days with a skeleton crew to check on what was happening in each compound—the Japanese, the German-Italian, and the guard compounds—Eifler inspected everything. One day he came across the Japanese internee leader who called himself "Admiral." He was swearing at noncommissioned officer Sgt. Lance Moran. The punishment was quick: seven days in solitary! And when "Admiral" returned to the camp, he was not allowed any other leadership role. Dr. Kazuo Miyamoto became the next "admiral."

Eifler's diary reads, for Dec. 30, 1941: "Admiral was disrespectful to Moran and I sentenced him to seven days solitary confinement."

Actually, Eifler served at Sand Island less than three months, for he was called by Washington, D.C. for a special assignment to lead an espionage team into Burma and China. But within these three months, he made his rules and character known. Stories on Eifler abound.

One story had to do with his thrift. When he saw guards and internees approach the garbage drum with left-over food, he asked himself, "How can we avoid having such waste of precious food?"

In a few days he had his answer. "Men," he said, "beginning with this meal, we will not serve you. You will serve yourself—buffet style. You can take whatever you want, in any amount. The only condition is, what you take, you eat. Whatever you have left over at any meal will be kept in the cooler with your name on the plate. At the next meal, you will eat your left-overs first, then you may go through the line for your regular meal. Is that understood?"

It was, but at first there were many plates in the cooler. Soon, however, the plates dwindled and men began taking only what they knew they could eat, going up for seconds if they were still hungry.

Shafter officials were both puzzled and pleased. How come the Sand Island food bill was so low? They came to investigate and commended Eifler for his initiative.

This thrift sometimes worked a hardship. One day an internee approached the garbage drum with what looked like a piece of meat on the plate.

"Finish your meal," Eifler said.

The internee who had been picked up without his dentures, pointed to his gums. But the order was, "Clean up your plate." The internee swallowed what looked like meat but was tendon and gristle. By evening the word filtered through the Japanese compound, "If you have bone or tough tendon, wrap it or hide it, or you may have to swallow it."

Eifler required a spoon, knife and fork count after each meal. Once, when a spoon was missing, Eifler demanded a "nude" inspection. Forty years later, Eifler insisted he would not have given such an order; he does not remember it. The internees, on the other hand, swear they were made to stand nude while their clothes and tents were examined. The lost silverware was not found in the Japanese compound. Kumaji Furuya, Yasutaro Soga, Kenkichi Fujimoto and Bishop Fujihana who stated emphatically that they were made to stand naked even remember the thoughts that passed through their mind. Fujimoto swore remembering that even in Japan, where nudeness in the community bath was commonplace, men were not made to stand naked in public view. Bishop Fujihana remembers best that that was the day some had received injections of some kind. Being kept naked in the hot sun and then in the ocean breeze after the injection resulted in a fever.

Eifler's diary reads, "Jan. 25, 1942. Found spoon on top of a cupboard in kitchen. Knife showed up in check. Found butter knife that had been found in a drain pipe the day before and not reported. Camp security has been very lax. Search turned up five watches, numerous rings—one valued at $3,000—a number of razor blades. Hope today will serve as a lesson for time to come."

The Rev. Ryoshin Okano case is also vivid in the minds of many.

"As we were returning from the garden patch outside the barbed wire fences, where we were raising lettuce, radishes and green onions, one of the guards saw Okano with a crude knife in his hand. The Rev. had made a tool by filing a piece of the thin metal band found around crates. Okano was not aware that such a tool would be considered dangerous. The guard blew a whistle; other guards came running. We all had to strip and be searched. Naturally almost all of us who worked in the garden had one of those "knives" which we found more useful in digging than pieces of sticks. There were of course only a few hoes and picks," Kenkichi Fujimoto explained.

"These could be used as knives and are therefore weapons. Besides, some of the metal is rusted. If you cut yourself, you'd be in trouble. You could get tetanus...lockjaw."

"How can we work in the garden without any tools?"

"Requisition for hoes," was the answer.

"We might get some next year...or the next..."

Lessons were quickly forgotten. A few days later, someone brought into camp a rusty pistol he had found while digging in the vegetable patch. Again Captain Eifler was furious. An internee with a pistol!

Of course it was rusted, the parts were frozen, and there were no bullets. Nevertheless, the idea of a weapon in an internee's hand was unthinkable, and Eifler went on and on for what seemed like hours. The other internees began complaining too. "Damn fool! Why didn't he rebury it? Didn't he know this would happen?"

Another time someone was found with money in his pocket. He had been examined in the nude and in his clothes many times. Where had the money come from? From the guards? But of course there were

44

secret places where one could hide things. Dr. Takahashi, for example, had a pin which he kept hidden protected in a *kiawe* tree. He used the pin to take out splinters for the men, and also when someone developed a pus-filled boil. What a basic all-around tool it was for a skilled physician! Yet, had Eifler found it, would he have taken it away as a possible "weapon"?

Once, two men were missing. How had they escaped the guards? When had they run off? What would happen to them if and when they were caught? Might they not be shot even before being captured? Each man looked for his friends in the line-up, and was grateful to see them. Who were the two who had escaped?

After all the fright and commotion, it was found that the guard had counted the men incorrectly. Eifler jingled his keys furiously and stalked off.

The humiliation, regimentation, fear and living conditions affected some of the men. One moaned he was not pregnant; he was sent to a hospital, then released. Others tried to commit suicide.

To counteract depression which followed their robot-like life, the men devised ways to find humor and to poke fun at their "captors." When roll was called, some would answer "Hair" instead of "Here!"

And when one man answered, "Yes, Sir" the others reprimanded him, saying, "Don't call him 'Sir.' He's just a common soldier. In England, 'Sir' is one who is knighted by the Queen. 'Sir' is to be used only when you respect someone highly."

Another prank was to use a substitute word for "prisoner." When the night guard called "Halt!" they had to answer "Prisoner," and they would be allowed to proceed to the latrine. One priest who couldn't remember the word said "Gardener," and was allowed to pass. Other favorites were "Poisoner!" and "Pissoner." In such childish ways they engaged in a battle of wits to keep themselves alert.

Although the internees did not know it then, both General Walter C. Short and Admiral Husband Kimmel had been retired or removed from active duty in the islands on Dec. 17. On Dec. 18, General Delos

SAND ISLAND: The camp was usually hot during the day, but when heavy rains fell, it often remained flooded for several days.

Top Photo Courtesy David R. Dingeman/ UH-Mānoa
Bottom Photo Courtesy U.S. Army Signal Corps.

C. Emmons was named new Hawai'i Commander of the Army and Admiral Chester Nimitz of the Navy.

General Emmons assured the people that their interned friends and relatives would not be mistreated and that an inspection of Sand Island Camp would be permitted by representative citizens.

On Dec. 20, only three days after Emmons' appointment, someone from his office visited Sand Island. Two days later, another officer met with the internees and told them that they were not criminals or prisoners, only detainees. After this officer's appearance, treatment of the internees improved.

Actually, the military chiefs of staff in Washington, D.C. had, by Dec. 19, 1941, put pressure on General Emmons to intern all Japanese in the islands, either by sending them to concentration camps on the Mainland or by placing them on one island—Moloka'i. The island with the former "leper" colony was named as a possible site. But Emmons responded that careful investigation had not found a single case of sabotage in Hawai'i, and the Japanese were vital to Hawai'i's economy since they provided much of the skilled labor. Incarceration of a third of Hawai'i's population would have resulted in serious manpower problems at this point in time.[2]

On January 30, 1942, when informed about another Cabinet meeting which again recommended mass removal of all Hawai'i Japanese to the Mainland, Emmons agreed but said transportation was not available.

On February 9, he received a War Department Order directing him to release all Japanese civilians employed by the Army. Emmons replied that there were no possible replacements, and shouldn't the Hawaiian situation be handled by those in Hawai'i? The War Department then cancelled its order.[3]

Then, on February 27, the Cabinet met a third time and Frank Knox, Secretary of the Navy, again raised the question of mass incarceration. The "defense of the islands is now carried out in the presence of a population predominantly with enemy sympathies and affiliations," Knox wrote to President Roosevelt.[4]

The recommendation of the Joint Chiefs of Staff in a March 11, 1942 addendum was that "all Japanese residents of the Hawaiian Islands (either U.S. citizens or aliens) be transported to the U.S. Mainland and placed under guard at a concentration camp..."[5]

But again the difficulty of mass evacuation was acknowledged by those in power. Also, Hawai'i's leaders did not exert the type of anti-Japanese pressure as was done in California. In fact, they exerted pressure to keep the Japanese in Hawai'i.

The men at Sand Island were unaware of these top-level activities. Their concerns were of a more personal nature. And, to their joy, some of the actions allowed were in their favor. For example, a few days before Christmas, they were allowed to use razors. Scraggly beards and itchy mustaches came off. The men felt cleaner, younger, and stronger. Then, as one good thing followed another, they were told they could send postcards home. But without any money to buy postcards or stamps, how could they do that?

Sgt. Launcelot Moran came to the rescue. On a trip to Honolulu, he purchased, with his own money, postcards and stamps for all of the internees. This was to be their first direct communication with wives and children. The card was the best Christmas gift they had ever had! Joy shone in their eyes, and they breathed and walked a little faster as they scribbled, in a few lines, their longing for home and their love and concern for the family.

Then, a little over three weeks after they had been picked up, they received a friendly visitor, the first allowed to speak to them in Japanese. He was Attorney Masaji Marumoto, who had been working for the past year with the FBI and community leaders to preserve order and harmony among ethnic groups in the community in the event of war. He was accompanied by Capt. Eifler and FBI Agent Harold Hughes as he talked to some of the internees.

Undoubtedly surprised to see them looking like beggars, for they had not yet had a change in clothing, Marumoto assured them he would see what he could do. A few days later cartons of clothes arrived for the internees.

The men spent day after day wondering when they were going to be released, when the military would finally decide they were innocent of any disloyal act to the United States. Sure enough, Rev. Jyosen Deme of Waipahu was called and he left.

Then, on Christmas Day, Rev. Chinpei Goto, a Christian minister, left, followed by 84-year-old Komeya.

Each day Kumaji Furuya waited to be called to the Hearing Board at the Immigration Office. Would it be today? Would he be able to meet his family tonight? Finally, at long last, his name was called.

Furuya gave his friends whatever he had that could be of some use: his soap, his handkerchief, his undershirt. In turn he was given messages to give to his friends' families, although the urgency was now missing, since soon all or almost all of them would be released.

Furuya was taken, again by barge, to the docks which were camouflaged and protected with machine guns. The luxury liner *Lurline* was painted a dark grey over its formerly gleaming white; instead of tourists, it now took families of military men back to the Mainland. The piers were barricaded. Despite all this, Furuya felt free and he took deep breaths of ocean air. Then, as they neared the pier, he saw some young men stacking boxes. One looked so much like his son, his heart thumped. Could it be? But then the youth turned; it was a Chinese boy.

He reported again to the Immigration Office interrogators. The examiner asked, "What is your occupation?"

"Owner, furniture store." Strange, for them to be asking more questions when they were about to release him.

"Who do you think will win this war? Which side do you want to win? Why did the Japanese bomb Pearl Harbor without declaration of war? Who gave Japan information regarding ships at Pearl Harbor? Why did you go to Japan three years ago? How much money did you donate to Japanese organizations last year? How much English education do you have?"

The next day he was asked the identical questions, this time in the presence of Honolulu *nisei* George Sakamaki and Oliver K. Yanaga. Why, he didn't know.

"Do you know Seiji Yoda of the Yamanashi Kenjinkai?"

"Yes." If he didn't know Yoda, why would they ask him this question?

Yoda was president of a *kenjinkai*. *Ken*, or province, is equivalent to a state, such as Oregon or Idaho; Japan had about 43 *kens* when the U.S. had 48 states. *Jin* means people, and *kai* is an organization. *Kenjinkai* therefore means an organization whose members are from a certain province in Japan. It was a friendship group. Members helped each other when there was a death in the family, during calamities such as floods and fires, or when a member was unemployed and looking for a job.

Together, members in such organizations held an annual summer picnic; this was a picnic for young and old, in an attempt to bind the generations together. The children—even toddlers—competed in races and sometimes dropped their diapers. Preteenagers ran the 3-legged race. The over-70 and -80 picked up cabbage and cucumbers and carefully trotted to the finish line. It was a fun time, with as many as four generations hugging a tree shade and sharing food, laughter, "talk-story," and free shaved ice.

Then there was the New Year's party, held within the first three months of the year. At this event, members were provided lucky numbers. The usual gift items garnered from business firms for the party were salt, toilet tissue, Kleenex and Ajax. Each family would get a sack filled with these items. Again, young and old could participate in simple games, such as Bingo.

Because newcomers to Hawai'i or plantation laborers were unable or unwilling to borrow money from banks at a high interest rate, the *ken* members participated in a *tanomoshi*. The *tanomoshi* was a form of a loan at a low interest rate. Unlike at a bank, no written contracts were necessary. If a person was accepted into the *tanomoshi* group, he was trusted as a fellow human being. It was better to have a friend pay low interest on a loan, instead of others giving him the money. This way, the borrower retained pride and integrity.

Yoda was president of one of these *kens* or organizations. "Yes, I know Yoda," Furuya repeated.

The next day was New Year's Eve. When Furuya's name was called, he was overjoyed. He might be able to spend New Year's Eve with his family...

Instead, he was issued a number: ISN-HJ-CI 188!

When he reported back to Sand Island with an embarrassed smile and a joke, someone returned his soap, another his undershirt, a third his handkerchief.

When Yasutaro Soga was called for interrogation at the Immigration Office, he was asked, "Are you pro-Japan?"

His spokesman, the Rev. Sidney Gulick, a highly respected religious figure who was Soga's character witness, answered, "I have known Soga since 1915. He is a man of integrity, a man who has worked for his community."

"That is not the question. Can you prove he is not anti-American?"

"I can vouch that he is not anti-American. But it is difficult to prove that, just as it would be difficult even for me to prove that I am not anti-American."

Then Soga was asked, "What do you think of the Greater East Asia Co-Prosperity Sphere?"

"I think Japan has a right to stand on her own feet."

Soga received number ISN-HJ-CI 305.

While at the Immigration Office, Furuya learned that Rev. Josen Deme had not been released at all. He had been placed in a German camp! An official in some office... surely not Sand Island for they could have easily verified this... had thought Josen Deme German and had transferred him to be with his own kind. The poor priest must have wondered why he was being placed with the Germans, Italians, and Austrians. The "Mixed Camp" in turn must have wondered if the Japanese in their midst was a German-speaking spy.

Those were days of alternating despondency and hope at the Immigration Station. One day someone would be released; another day someone would be returned to Sand Island with a number. The uncertainty was worse than knowing definitely that one was to be detained for the duration of the war. A book store merchant, unable to bear the pressure, slashed his left wrist with a razor. Although the others were sympathetic and understood how he felt, they also were indignant, for MPs came and confiscated the razors they had finally been allowed to keep. "So much trouble for the rest of us," they complained. "If he wants to die, there must be other ways." Even two months of internment had hardened some of them.

Sundays were special days at Sand Island. Church services were held.

It wasn't services that made it special; it was the fact that the men could attend services with the women. There were several women interned: Mrs. Ishiko Mori, supposedly a *Yomiuri Shinbun* correspondent, but really a housewife who posed as a newspaperwoman so that she could remain in Hawai'i with her husband. Yoshie and Yuki Miyao, one the mother and the other the wife of Shinto priest Shigemaru Miyao, were there, as well as Haru Tanaka, a part-time agent for the Japanese Consulate and a Japanese language school teacher. Others were Mrs. Shizuyo Takechi, a part-time worker in a newspaper office; Mrs. Shin-sho

Hirai and Mrs. Miyuki Kawasaki, priestesses; Mrs. Umeno Harada, from the island of Ni'ihau; Mrs. Haruko and Mrs. Yasue Takahashi, and Mrs. Menzen Ito. The women were cared for by Mrs. Eifler, who invited them to dinner occasionally and supplied their needs as best she could. To the men interned, the 11 women in the camp represented their own wives and daughters, so when they learned of this kind treatment, they relented in their dislike of Eifler. Surely a man with such a kind wife could not be that bad. Perhaps, they discussed among themselves, Capt. Eifler was dominating and seemingly cruel because he himself was insecure, being a German haunted by Nazism and Hitlerism.

To the internees, however, Eifler remained "one mean bugger." What they didn't realize was that Eifler fought for their welfare relentlessly. For example, the water line to the camp was once cut when a freighter's anchor accidentally ruptured it. Because the clogged toilets presented a health hazard, and no cooking or showering could be done, Eifler instructed his men to hook the pipes to the main water line. This bypassed the meter.

"Under what authority are you doing this?" a member of the harbormaster's crew demanded.

Eifler pulled out his .45 automatic. "You will leave the line connected. The detainees and soldiers on this island will not be subjected to a health hazard. Tell your boss to speak to my boss." The crew member retreated.

The water line took two weeks to be repaired, but Eifler made sure water was available in the camp. At the risk of being censured and even demoted, he had acted as he judged necessary for the welfare of those on the island.

At one time, the men decided not to work in the gardens. But sitting on their cots without any activity caused constipation.

Eifler asked himself, "How can I get the men to move around more to prevent constipation and other illnesses? How can we prevent this boredom which is bound to breed mischief and problems?"

He decided to have some forms printed. Anyone who wanted to work in the garden outside or to engage in construction work, for two-story barracks were being built to replace the tents in which the internees lived, would have to apply for permission to do so. The men would have to be screened.

"When it became a privilege, not an order, to work in the gardens or in construction work, the men competed to be on the list," Eifler remembers. "Also, they followed the rules and guidelines very faithfully, once they knew what these were."

One day the internees buzzed angrily. The Hawai'i internees could not speak to Kazuo Sakamaki, U.S.'s Pacific War Prisoner #1, but they could see him. Sakamaki lived within his "birdcage," an enclosure with a tiny house in it. He ate and slept there, and walked around the wire fence for his exercise. One day he appeared with burns on his face.

"He was mistreated," the internees said.

"No," Sgt. Moran, who took food to Sakamaki three times a day, said. "Check the burns. In what shape are they?"

When they looked closely, they found that the burns were in the shape of an inverted triangle on one cheek. That, the internees were told, was a mark of disgrace. Sakamaki was scheduled to have his picture taken the next day. He had burned himself that night with his one cigarette a day to show the Japanese nation that he had not fulfilled his goal, his duty, his responsibility. He had disgraced himself by having his mini-sub captured, by not having fired the two torpedoes he carried, by having his ship-mate drown. He wanted the Japanese military to know that he knew he had failed, he had disgraced himself.

The Japanese internees gradually began realizing they would have to learn all the facts of any incident, not rush to a conclusion. What seemed to be true on this side of the barbed wire fence was not necessarily true on the other side of the fence.

On March 1, 1942, Eifler was ordered to another assignment, a dangerous one involving espionage in the jungles of Burma and China. Washington D.C. even overrode General Emmons' statement that Eifler was needed in Hawai'i.

"At Sand Island and elsewhere I acted according to the ethics of my profession," Eifler explained later. "In the final analysis, I have to judge myself, for I have to live with myself. I was not sent to Sand Island or any other war zone to win popularity contests. I went as an American officer, responsible for the lives of my own men and for the lives entrusted to me...in the case of Sand Island, the Japanese, German, Italian and other internees.

"I wanted to prevent suicides because of temporary intense depression. I wanted to prevent escapes, which might mean someone could be shot or killed. I wanted to safeguard the health of the detainees, for they were not criminals. I made rules and regulations which were then non-existent, for I needed a system of behavior in the camp." One day, before he left for his new assignment, he received a letter from a German internee who had been transferred from Sand Island to Camp McCoy in Wisconsin. The internee wrote:

> Dear Capt. Eifler:
>
>> ...I thank you again for the way you treated us at Sand Island—strict but just and fair. You tried to make men out of us in a military manner and I am sure it did me a load of good. Sometimes I hated you for it, but I understand now. As an Officer of the United States Army you did your duty well...
>>
>> Helmut Emig[6]

It was on March 9, 1942, soon after the first contingent of internees had left for the Mainland and the day after Captain Eifler left for another assignment that an internee died. Hisahiko Kokubo, a store owner and president that year of Kauaʻi's Kumamoto Kenjinkai, was from Waimea, Kauaʻi. He had suffered a heart attack.

The Red Cross hastened to assist in getting medical attention but it was too late. Instead of an ambulance, it was a hearse that was needed. Suddenly, the internees realized that some of them might never see their families again. To be incarcerated and deprived of conveniences was one thing; to die without seeing wife and children again was another!

When the coffin was being taken by hearse to the barge, the internees gathered at the barbed wire gate to bid farewell to someone whom they had known so intimately for the past few months. They felt doubly sad, for the coffin was bare, almost as if the man himself was naked. They looked around the compound for some flowers, some greens to place on the coffin. There was none. There was only sand and some *kiawe* trees.

Then Sgt. Moran—the same Moran who had bought each of them a postcard and stamp at Christmas—went to a bougainvillea bush outside the compound. He plucked twigs of lavender-magenta blossoms and placed them on the coffin. Now they could bid farewell to a friend properly. They bowed once to their friend Kokubo and once to a compassionate fellow-man, Sgt. Moran. Their hearts welled with love for this towering 6'2" bushy-haired Irishman who was so much like an overgrown teenager, eager to assist anyone and everyone, even the "enemy."

Early in the morning of February 17, a whistle blew. Furuya and the others ran out and lined up as usual.

Captain Eifler announced, "Those whose names we call, get all your belongings and stand in one corner of the yard."

They could go home! This time they could really go home! In all 172 names were called. Furuya, Fujimoto, Otani and Dr. Miyamoto were to leave. Soga was one of 30 to remain.

The 172 boarded the barge in groups and chattered loudly, like mynah birds on banyan trees in the evening. But at the Immigration Office they were puzzled to see piles of cartons and some suitcases with their names on them. What were in the cartons and why hadn't these been delivered to them at Sand Island where they could have made good use of extra clothing?

Before they could go upstairs to the now familiar room, they were photographed and fingerprinted. The photos had numbers on them, like convict pictures. Furuya was #188, theater manager Masayuki Chikuma 260 and Rev. Josen Deme 117. Number "1" belonged to the Japan navy skipper Kazuo Sakamaki of the midget sub that had gone aground at Bellows Field on Dec. 7.

It took from 4 p.m. to 4 a.m. to complete the picture-taking and fingerprinting. Before they had time to sleep, they were called to breakfast. It was drizzling at 7 a.m. but they had to stand in line and eat again from the familiar and detested tin trays.

At 8:30 a.m. Attorney Masaji Marumoto arrived with five others; Masatoshi Katagiri, Ernest Isao Murai, Baron Yasuo Goto, Shigeo Yoshida and Katsumi Kometani. Marumoto gave them news that stunned most of them. They were to be sent to the Mainland!

They listened, numb with shock, as Marumoto told them they could take only what they could carry. Everything was to go in one duffel bag; space on the boat was limited. The military would issue each a heavy overcoat and a pair of sturdy shoes, for they would be going to a cold climate. Their money—each person was allowed $50—would be given to them at point of destination. (This money was destined never to be received.)

On February 20, at about 9 a.m., the men boarded trucks which would take them to the pier. As Dr. Kazuo Miyamoto described it, "Three soldiers with shotguns were on each truck...all the soldiers wore steel helmets and were in battle array. Three armored cars with anti-aircraft guns formed a part of the procession and were stationed at the front, middle and end. Non-commissioned officers on motorcycles and sidecars paraded back and forth giving orders or just moving around."[7]

In later departures of groups of internees, which left March 20, May 23, June 21, August 6, September 16 and October 10 in 1942, as well as others in 1943, families lined the short street, hoping to catch a glimpse of husband or father. "*Ganbatte! Ganbatte!* Don't give up...don't give up!" It was like a funeral procession, with tears streaming down so many faces.

But at the February 20 departure, there was not a single soul on the street. It was like dying, when each has to go alone, although in the midst of others.

CHAPTER 5

THE NI'IHAU TRAGEDY:

Which Comes First, Man or Enemy?

Southwest of Kaua'i, on the tiny island of Ni'ihau, two Japanese families and about 180 Hawaiians lived on the Robinson Ranch. The ranch was really all of 48–square mile Ni'ihau, since Aylmer Robinson owned the island.

The residents of Ni'ihau had no daily interisland transportation and no communication facilities such as telephone or radio. Those who chose to live there had to be content to live simply, in tune with sea, sky, and earth. In exchange, they led peaceful, healthy lives.

Once a week a sampan came from Kaua'i, twenty miles away, to Ki'i Landing, close to the island's northern tip. The Hawaiians lived at Pu'uwai, 15 miles from Ki'i Landing and about midway on the island.

The Robinsons lived on a plateau in a home at Ki'eki'e, about two miles south of Pu'uwai.

One of the two Japanese families was that of Ishimatsu Shintani, 60, an *issei* married to a Hawaiian; they had three children. Born in Japan in 1881, Shintani had emigrated to Hawai'i on Jan. 24, 1900 at age 19. His major responsibility on the ranch was to care for the hives of bees on the island.

The other Japanese family was that of Yoshio Harada, 39, and his wife Umeno. They were *nisei*. They had three children, ages 7, 6 and 4.

When the Haradas were first approached by beekeeper Kurihara to work on Ni'ihau, as he was retiring, the Haradas refused. After all, they had just built a home on Kaua'i and their two children would be in elementary school.

Mr. Robinson, impressed with Harada, would not accept "no" for an answer. He came to talk to Umeno Harada personally to convince her that five years on the island would benefit them financially. Besides, they wouldn't have to live in the servants' quarters. They could live in the ranch manager's home which had been brought lovingly, piece by piece, from Scotland and rebuilt for the elderly Scot caretaker.

"But what happens if my daughter becomes ill? There aren't any doctors on Ni'ihau," Umeno asked.

"On the other hand, no one gets sick on Ni'ihau," Aylmer Robinson explained. "Before anyone can come to Ni'ihau—and that is only with permission that is very seldom granted—he must have a physical checkup by a doctor. Even the weekly supplies are fumigated before they are brought ashore. So we don't have the diseases the other islanders have."

"What about a toothache? Or appendicitis?"

"We can send signals to Kaua'i to send a boat immediately."

"How?"

"By building a large fire on the high point of the island. My people on Kaua'i are always on the lookout for such a signal. Besides, we have rowboats for emergencies."

"What would we do?"

"You, Harada, would help with the bee hives and other necessary chores. Mrs., you would cook and care for the main house. We have a caretaker there who manages the ranch, and when he retires at the end of next year, who knows, you may be selected to manage the ranch, Harada."

Finally the Haradas agreed to try it for a period of five years. They sold their home to a sister at cost, and moved to an island so dry water was more precious than money to the villagers. And, anyway, on an island without a regular store, who needed much money?

The Haradas had been on Ni'ihau for a year, with the two older children in elementary school on the island of Kaua'i, when, on Dec. 7, 1941, a Japanese plane piloted by a Shigenori Nishikaichi crashlanded near Pu'uwai. The Haradas were having lunch at the Robinson ranch and they heard a plane flying low but didn't bother to look out the window.

It was about 2 p.m. when a Hawaiian boy on a horse galloped toward the Robinson home.

"Mr. Harada, Mr. Harada...a plane crashed near the village. The pilot, he's Japanese. Please come..." He went galloping back.

Quickly the Haradas harnessed a horse and carriage—actually a cart—and drove to the village. Was the pilot from Kaua'i or Honolulu? Was he hurt badly? They must signal Kaua'i immediately for medical help if the pilot was injured, they decided.

But when they reached the plane, already surrounded by curious Hawaiians, they were astounded to see a Japanese pilot beside a plane with the rising sun insignia on wings and body.

"Who are you? Where did you come from? Don't be afraid. My name is Harada Yoshio, and this is my wife and child," Harada said in his inadequate Japanese.

Left: Yoshio Harada of Niʻihau, Hawaiʻi.
Right: Shigenori Nishikaichi of Japan, who crashlanded on Niiahu
December 7, 1941 soon after bombing Pearl Harbor.

Photo Courtesy David R. Dingeman

The youth bowed. "My name is...my name is...is... Nishikaichi Shigenori, from Japan. Is this place Ni'ihau?"

"That's right. But what are you doing here? And on that tiny plane?"

For one fleeting moment, Umeno Harada thought, "And has your plane been fumigated, and have you had a physical checkup?" But she merely exchanged a bow of greeting.

"I...I must admit that I'm on my way home from attacking Pearl Harbor," the pilot admitted.

"Pearl Harbor! Our Pearl Harbor?"

"Yes. And when my engine began sputtering, I decided to land here, on Ni'ihau, as we were instructed. A sub will pick us up within 24 hours. Would I be safe here for that length of time?"

"Your life will be safe, but tomorrow, on Monday, a boat will come from Kaua'i with our food and other supplies. At that time you will have to report to Kaua'i for a medical check-up and to the military authorities. By the way, how many of you attacked Pearl Harbor?"

"Over 300 planes..."

"300! Why, this means war between Japan and the United States!"

"I'm sorry...May I still wait here until someone comes for me?"

"There's nothing else you or we can do. There's no transportation to the outside world from Ni'ihau and no communication system. To get Kaua'i's attention we build a large fire in case of emergency. But since a boat is coming tomorrow anyway, we won't have to signal Kaua'i. You will have to go to that island on the return trip, since this is a private island and you cannot remain here without permission from the owner, Mr. Robinson."

Harada explained to the Hawaiians what had taken place. They formed a large circle, and when darkness fell, they lighted a kerosene lamp.

"Umeno, go home and cook some food for us. We'll all wait here until the sampan comes in tomorrow."

"No need do that," the Hawaiians said. "We got enough food for everybody."

The scheduled boat did not appear the following day, as, unknown to them, all boats were forbidden to leave any port in the Hawaiian Islands. Neither did the Japanese Navy's rescue sub come for Nishikaichi, the pilot. Guarded by about four or five Hawaiians, he spent that night and the next waiting for some form of transportation.

There were, however, ranch responsibilities to which Harada had to tend. After all, he was now in charge of the island since the death in September of the elderly Scot manager. Harada had been promised the managership beginning January 1, 1942, but already he took responsibility for the ranch, working twelve to fifteen hours a day, almost as if the ranch were his own.

"Listen," Harada told the Hawaiians, "what if we take the pilot to the ranch house, and some of you can stay and guard him. I have work to do."

That seemed reasonable enough, so a cart was sent for, since the pilot still seemed dazed from the plane crash. At the ranch, Harada put Nishikaichi into his own bed, where the pilot slept in exhaustion for over ten hours.

When he awoke, his mind was clearer. "My map...my documents..." were his first words. "Where are they?"

"What map? What documents?" Harada asked. "I didn't see any. Were they on the plane?"

"No. In my pocket. I must get them back. They're important. They're more important than my life."

Harada consulted the Hawaiians. Yes, one of the Hawaiians had the documents, they explained.

"I'll ask Shintani-san to go to the village and get them..."

But the Hawaiians refused to give the papers to Shintani. They would give them only to Mr. Robinson or to military officials, now that

Japan and the U.S. were at war. Shintani relayed the message, then disappeared to hide with some of the Hawaiians. They knew Nishikaichi was armed and therefore dangerous.

The pilot spent part of his time talking about Japan—his parents, his younger brother, his village school. "Have you been to Japan?" he asked Harada.

"No, never. But my parents came from Japan and they talked about their home and farm. I think they loved Japan, but they didn't want to leave Hawai'i because their children were here."

They spent hours talking about what would happen now there was a war.

"At least we'll be safe here, my wife, daughter and I," Harada said. "As safe as any other spot in the world. Who would want to bomb an island with less than 200 people? And I'm 39, almost 40, too old to be drafted. Besides, my boss, Mr. Robinson, needs me here. But I hope the war doesn't drag on, because my son is 6 years old..."

As the days passed, and they now waited for next Monday's boat—what had happened to last Monday's boat?—Nishikaichi's eyes grew wilder and wilder, and he became more tense. Finally, he said, "I'm going to the village to find my papers. I must get them or die in the attempt. My life means nothing, if the disgrace of having the maps and documents stolen is to follow me all my life. I wouldn't be able to return to my country, if I don't destroy those papers."

"Wait, Nishikaichi-san. I'll go with you. Maybe if I asked the Hawaiians and explained the situation, they will give the documents to me. They've always listened to me, obeyed me. Let me ask them."

"I have my gun, Mr. Harada. I intend to use it if necessary. Once I get those documents, I'll go anywhere. I can't impose on you any longer."

"Yes, you must report to Kaua'i. I'll ask the Hawaiians to build a signal fire. I'll borrow a gun from Mr. Robinson's collection and try and help you get the papers."

"Daddy, I don't think..." Mrs. Harada warned, but already the two men were slipping out a back door while the watchmen were eating and drinking.

The village was deserted, for everyone had gone into hiding. Nishikaichi and Harada searched the home of the man who was supposed to have the documents.

"I can't find it," Nishikaichi said. "I'm going to burn the house down. Maybe the documents are here somewhere."

"No, no!" protested Harada, but it was too late. The bone-dry wood went up in flames.

Unknown to them, two Hawaiians—Benjamin Kanahele and his wife—were hiding in the village. When they saw the wanton burning, Benjamin charged the pilot. The two grappled, but Nishikaichi was no match for the tall and husky Hawaiian. The pilot fired three times, wounding the Hawaiian. At this point, Kanahele "lost his temper" and, grabbing Nishikaichi by his feet, dashed his head against a stone wall. Harada, for reasons unknown, put his borrowed gun to himself and pulled the trigger.

When a military boat reached Ni'ihau, alerted by two men who had secretly rowed to Kaua'i with news of what was happening on Ni'ihau, it was all over. Lt. Jack Mizuha of the 299th Infantry, 13 enlisted men, and Aylmer Robinson landed at Nonopapa, only a few miles from Pu'uwai. It was also a prelude to heartbreak and suffering for Ishimatsu Shintani, the other innocent Japanese on the island, for Mrs. Harada, and especially for the three children who had to carry the stigma of "traitor father" for many years to come.

The elderly Shintani had not cooperated with the pilot. Instead, he had fled with the other Hawaiians. Yet he was questioned by the FBI and interned for four years, presumably because he had Japanese blood or he was a Japanese alien.

Those four years—1,460 days—must have been lonely years for Shintani, ISN-HJ-CI 1800, eating in crowded messhalls where friends shared the last cup of coffee or a cigarette among themselves; and sleeping within touching distance of men who talked in sibilant Japanese instead of soothing Hawaiian about politics, philosophy, history and economics but not about the ranch or Niʻihau.

He returned after WWII to his beloved islands and even became a naturalized American at age 79. His certificate, so proudly treasured, was numbered 7898993; it was assurance that he would not be abruptly incarcerated again.

Perhaps, before he died Nov. 23, 1970, at age 89, the four years of internment merged with his other memories. Perhaps he did not wonder whether, had he been able to convince the Hawaiians on Niʻihau who had the maps and documents from the plane to give them to him or to destroy them in front of the pilot, his friend Harada would still be alive. Perhaps Harada's wife would not have been interned. Perhaps Harada's children would not have been cut off from their parents. Perhaps...perhaps...so much pain was incurred because a 21-year-old pilot had crashed on Niʻihau instead of in the ocean, where his maps and documents would have been safe and he himself would have been honored as a war hero who had died bombing Pearl Harbor!

Mrs. Harada, back at the ranchhouse that Dec. 14, 1941, did not know what had happened at the village until one of the Hawaiians rode up to tell her what had taken place. Had she looked out of the window earlier, she would have seen a boat coming in the direction of Nonopapa, a few miles south. She had ordered some Christmas goods and had been anxious to get them, with Christmas only ten days away. When her husband and the pilot had sneaked away the day before, she had been concerned, but had not expected the tragedy that followed.

A furious Aylmer Robinson reached the ranchhouse and gave Mrs. Harada one hour to pack her things and get out of Niʻihau. Dazed, not able to believe her husband was dead, she numbly collected some of her daughter's clothes. The rest of her things would be packed and sent later, Mr. Robinson assured her. She and her daughter must take the boat back to Kaua'i immediately. Thus began a painful journey for a woman who lost husband, job and prized possessions all within an hour's time.

Umeno was taken first to Intelligence Headquarters at the Kaua'i Armory, where she was quizzed thoroughly. Then she was driven to the Wailua County Jail, while her daughter was taken by a probation officer to a relative's home.

After two months at Wailua Jail, where the questioning continued, she was sent to the Honolulu Immigration Station. The room to her right was occupied by Otto Kuehn, the German who was supposed to have been a spy for the Japanese government. The room on her left was the large room with the 75 or so male Japanese internees. During breakfast, lunch and dinner she was able to relate her story to them, each time her tears flowing uncontrollably. Her greatest grief, she said, was that her husband's body was on Ni'ihau, hastily buried together with that of the pilot. None of the relatives had been able to have services over his grave.

"To what sect of Buddhism do you belong?" the priests asked her. When she told them, they said, "We will hold a service for your husband tonight. We do not have incense, candles or gong, but your husband's spirit will know that he is being accompanied to Heaven with our prayers and your love. Whatever his reason was, killing himself with a bullet instead of defending his actions with words, no one can ever know. And since we don't and can't know, it is useless to surmise. Instead, let us send his spirit heavenward for he was a good husband, father, worker and friend for 39 years. His last day or last week is for God to decide."

This was when Umeno Harada's tears fell peacefully. Her tears in the future would be for her children and the pain they must suffer, not for herself or for her husband.

When she was transferred to Sand Island, she felt better for there were other women there. Then, on Sundays, when the men came over to the women's end for Sunday services, she saw several people she knew from Kaua'i. One was Rev. Shigeo Fujino, a Shinto priest.

She was surprised one Sunday to find Rev. Fujino was allowed to eat lunch with her. "I'm your cousin," he whispered, "on our mother's side. They allow relatives to have lunch together on Sundays." Indeed the two were distant relatives.

When Sand Island was closed in 1943 and the internees had the option of being sent to the Mainland to War Relocation Authority camps or to Honouliuli Internment Camp near 'Ewa on O'ahu, she wrote to her sister on Kaua'i:

> I would like to take the children with me to a Mainland camp. I am so lonesome without them. I can work for $16 a month, plus each of us would have a $3.50 monthly allowance for staples. I am sure I can get by. I am so lonesome!

But her sister and other relatives refused. "The children are attending school and they have friends here. What if something happens to you? If you become ill? What would the children do? No, better to leave them on Kaua'i, where there are many relatives. That way, someone will always be able to care for them. I know it is lonesome for you, but all of us are having to make some sacrifices and bear needless pain. This includes the children. So you must endure your loneliness for a little while longer."

Mrs. Harada decided to remain at Honouliuli. Luckily, after 30 months—900 days—the women's compound was needed for the Japan POWs from various Pacific battles, and Mrs. Harada and the few women left were paroled so space could be used more efficiently.

Paroled, she found her battle had only begun. She found her household goods on Niʻihau had been shipped back to Kauaʻi, but many items were missing. She wrote to Mr. Robinson for help in collecting money the Hawaiians owed her, but he refused. She turned to the only thing she knew—sewing.

She sewed all day and through the night till after midnight. Her ten-year-old daughter cooked dinner for the four of them. "Ganbare, ganbare...hang on tight, keep on going..." she encouraged herself. "Ganbare, ganbare..." her foot-operated sewing machine echoed.

She refused to feel guilty, to carry the label of "traitor." "My husband paid the penalty for his actions, whatever his motives were that last day. He gave his life for someone whom he hardly knew, but who was a human being before he was a friend or enemy. Is loyalty to country stronger than kindness to a human being who is right there before you?

"My husband paid the supreme penalty. Crucify him and crucify me, if you must, but don't crucify the helpless children. Haven't they suffered enough? At their age, do they deserve this type of punishment? Can't you judge each individual separately? Must my children bear their father's burden all their lives?"

Mrs. Harada remembered how, one evening, as the pilot sat talking with her husband over the kitchen table at the Robinson ranch, he said, "In school I heard about Hawaiʻi. I always dreamed of coming here some day, maybe on my honeymoon, or after I had worked seven or nine years in a company. The ocean is such a beautiful blue and purple, instead of slate gray as at home. Do you know, I carried bombs on my plane, but as I was coming over the island, I heard Japanese music on the radio. A little girl was singing a doyo, a lullaby. And the thought crossed my mind: What if I kill this innocent child? But I was trained as a military man. I had a mission to accomplish. There was no turning back. I dropped my bombs on the targets—direct hits—and turned away from the destruction as fast as I could. I knew there would be rejoicing on the carrier that night because of the success of the bombing, but I couldn't rejoice. I was born on a country farm. I lived a simple life. I was conscripted, as were all the other young people on surrounding farms. I trained hard, just as I had studied hard at school and worked hard at home. I was selected for this project because of my marksmanship, and now here I am. Strange, I feel close to God. If I am destined to die soon, I would like to die here. And I want to thank you for you have been my friend, even though you know I'm the enemy."

When Mrs. Harada was paroled from Honouliuli Camp, her brother-in-law asked if he could help in any way.

"Yes, I'd like to get Yoshio from Ni'ihau. I know he would prefer to be here on Kaua'i with us."

Mr. Robinson agreed to this request. The Board of Health also wanted the pilot's body brought out, and this required a few months of negotiating and waiting. Finally, one day, her brother, her brother-in-law, a cousin, a mortician, and a Caucasian sergeant went to Ni'ihau for the bodies. Since there was no identification of the site, it took some searching to find the grave, but finally the bodies were found.

There was only one metal casket. Where would they put the pilot?

The Caucasian sergeant took off his jacket and carefully placed the remains of the pilot in it. He put the bones into the airtight casket for the return trip to Kaua'i.

The pilot's body was later sent to Japan to his hometown on another island, Shikoku, which he hadn't wanted to leave. Harada had returned to his home, Kaua'i, which he too hadn't wanted to leave.

Now the two men, as well as the two nations, were at peace.

CHAPTER 6

THE KALĀHEO STOCKADE:

In a Lush Valley

Somewhere in the lush mountains between Līhuʻe and Hanapēpē on Kauaʻi, the island closest to tiny Niʻihau, was a structure large enough to house about 20–25 people. Adjacent to this building was a messhall, showers and latrines. A Boy Scout Camp? It could have been, except that the officials and guards wore military garb, were armed with handguns, and traveled in military jeeps.

It was a peaceful site, back in early 1942, except for the persistent whine of mosquitoes. As soon as one opened the door of a building, a swarm of zebra-striped mosquitoes sneaked in and hid under the cots, which were lined in two straight rows, waiting for the dark. The bolder and hungrier mosquitoes attacked even during daylight hours.

Luckily, mosquitoes could not distinguish captor from captive, so officials and internees alike were cooperatively battling the never-ending horde of miniature vampires, and the energy of the guards was distracted toward a natural rather than a man-made enemy.

When insuranceman Paul Shizuo Muraoka was taken to Kalāheo Stockade, as the structure was called, he checked immediately to see if others were there. They were!

Paul had just spent a month in solitude, locked in the Līhuʻe Plantation Gymnasium shower room. He saw another human being three times a day: morning, noon and evening, when a guard brought him his food. Had he not had his food, he would have thought they had forgotten him, locked alone, in, of all places, a shower room. He wondered why he had been picked up for detention, why he had been locked in this shower room instead of at Wailua County Jail, and how long he would have to remain here.

Recollecting his past years, Paul could only surmise as to why he had been picked up by the FBI. He had lived in Japan from 1932 to 1934, the post-Depression years, and on his return had worked at the Japanese Consulate in Honolulu for six months, helping to take a census of Japanese in the territory. Perhaps his name had been taken from some old list found at the Consulate. The fact that he had been expatriated from Japan evidently carried no weight.

When he was transferred from solitary confinement in the Gym to Kalāheo Stockade, he could once again talk to other human beings—to Mr. Senda, the photographer; to Shinobu Taketa, the plumber, and others. It was then that he was able to eat musubi and other food his wife brought on visitation days.

When, after a year at the Stockade, he was told he could be reunited with his wife if he would move to a Mainland Relocation Camp, he agreed. Because he was an American citizen, he would be sent to a War Relocation Center from which he could be released if he found a job.

Together, he and his wife were shipped to Jerome Relocation Center in Arkansas. There his wife worked in a hospital, and Paul himself was elected manager of his block. With the $36 they jointly earned each month, they bought tools, clothes, and other necessities, using either the Sears or the Montgomery Ward catalogues.

Always an entrepreneur and learning that chickens could be purchased live for 10¢ a head, Paul finagled a pass to a chicken farm and purchased as many chickens as he and some friends could manage. They cut small holes in burlap bags and carried about six chickens in each bag, with their heads sticking out.

From this stock, Paul patiently raised chicks until eventually he was dubbed "Chicken King" of the camp. Barbed wire and machine guns could not fetter his imagination, determination and gambling instincts which paid off well.

One day he and a friend received a pass to a small town where purchases could be made. There, in the window of a hole-in-the-wall store, he saw a type of candy he had not seen for many many years. It was a golden taffy, filled with peanuts, covered with sesame seeds and cut into an oblong. He remembered an old Chinese man on Kaua'i, with pole on back, who had carried two baskets of goodies, one on each end of the pole. One basket carried manapua and pepeiao; the other basket included the sesame candy.

Mouth watering, they entered the store. But when the Chinese man saw them in their camp garb, he said, "I no sell enemy."

"But we're not enemy! We're not from Japan. We're from Hawai'i."

The man pointed to the clothes. "You Japanee? You prisoner?"

"Well, Japanese in blood, but we're American citizens…"

"Japaneee bomb China too…you enemy…" The man sat down and picked up a magazine.

Had the storekeeper been a haughty Southern white, the type they saw in movies, they could have expected this. But from a fellow Asian, an immigrant? Surely he too had met many undeserved prejudices in the past! Or was he more fearful than any of the other town merchants because of his race and the prejudices he had met? Paul Muraoka and his friend walked out into the street. They couldn't wait to get back to camp.

Paul's Kauaʻi friend Shinobu Taketa also left for Jerome, Arkansas at about the same time. Taketa, an American citizen, had been educated in Japan. He had been three when his mother took him to Hiroshima and 18 when he returned to Hawaiʻi in 1935. While working at his father's plumbing shop, he had been asked to work on an Office of Civilian Defense project. Patriotically, he went. The project ended November, 1942, and within a month, Taketa was interrogated, placed in Kalāheo Stockade, then sent to Jerome on Dec. 26, 1942 with his wife. It had been freezing cold in the hastily completed barracks, but at least he was with his wife and they could depend upon one another.

Taketa often wondered whether he had made the right decision at Jerome when the Army asked him two questions from a long list of other questions. One was, "Are you a loyal citizen of the United States?"

"Of course I am," he had answered.

"Would you volunteer to serve in the U.S. Army?" was the next question.

"Yes, but only if you send my wife and child home to Hawaiʻi," he answered. "I don't want my wife living here alone. It's not a desirable environment."

"You don't stipulate the conditions! We do!" the interrogator answered.

"If that's the case, and it means my wife, child and I can go to Japan together, I'll renounce my U.S. citizenship. It hasn't done much to protect me anyway. I want my family kept together. That is the most important thing in the world for me."

Sent to Tule Lake where all the "disloyals" or those not considered loyal to the U.S. were to be kept in one camp, he found that the "renunciants" were strong members of *Hoshi-dan*, a group of pro-Japan internees. Since he was to be sent to Japan anyway, he decided to join this group, although he heard that Rev. Kenjitsu Tsuha of Honolulu and some other leaders of the *Hoshi-dan* had been sent to an isolation camp called Leupp, in Arizona. That camp, someone reported, had 150 guards watching over 70 internees. Other luckier *Hoshi-dan* members had been sent to Bismarck, North Dakota.

Like the others in *Hoshi-dan*, Taketa cut his hair short, wore a head-band with the Rising Sun insignia painted on it, practiced calisthenics, jogged around the field early in the morning, and bowed to the rising sun on his knees.

It was November 26, 1945, when Taketa left Seattle for Japan. By then he knew about the atom bombs dropped on Hiroshima and Nagasaki. He knew Japan had admitted defeat. He knew there was a food shortage, starvation, and suffering. But he was strong and healthy. He could work on his relatives' rice paddies and vegetable field and repay them for their immediate support.

He did not see his fellow Kalāheo Stockade friends—Hisashi Fujimoto, who had been sent to Gila, Arizona; or Kazuto Yokota, who had been heard from while at Lordsburg and at Santa Fe, New Mexico. Had they elected to return to Hawai'i, or would they be moving to Japan ?

The remnants of destruction Taketa saw in Hiroshima and the scarred atom bomb victims made him realize he had been right in not actively becoming a part of war.

He reached the lonely train station in Hiroshima at 1:30 in the morning, and rather than wait six hours for a bus, he decided to walk. It took him five hours, carrying his worldly belongings, to walk to Ka'be, deep in the mountains. It was 6:30 when he reached the farm home he had left so many years ago when he was 18!

With daylight, he began to see maimed and scarred men, women and children—men and women bent with age but carrying also the penalties of war. The children, including those not yet of school age, were they to live a lifetime with such disfigurement? Twisted faces with one eye on a slant to the other, loss of hair, crooked backs…Taketa was overcome with nausea, then felt ashamed of his weakness. War was not fair. He, an adult male, had lived a protected four years in a desert camp. These young children did not even know what the war was about, or why their lives had suddenly been changed from home and playground activities to constant pain and pitying looks. War was no longer a romantic engagement between samurai or knights in armor. War included young and old, the armed and the unarmed, the sick and the healthy, male and female. So this was the beginning of a new era in warfare!

Taketa spent the days working and waiting for his family to follow him to Japan, as had been promised. Each time a ship was scheduled to arrive from the United States, he walked the many miles to Kurihama Harbor to check if his family was on board. "Ganbare, Ganbare!" he encouraged himself. They'll come soon, and we can be a family unit again. Maybe, when the family comes, I can go to the city and my knowledge of English will help me get a good job and we can rebuild our lives…

Finally it was announced that the last ship with American evacuees was to arrive in March, 1946. He peered anxiously at each person walking down the gangplank, but his wife was not on. What had happened?

Then he saw a woman, a Mrs. Uemura, whom he and his wife had known in camp. He rushed to her, happy to see a familiar face. But Mrs. Uemura had bad news…his wife and two children would not be returning to Japan. At the last minute, his wife had decided that the children, being so young, should live where they would have nutritious food, medical care, uninterrupted education, and a loving atmosphere. They had therefore gone to live with Taketa's father, who still maintained a plumbing business on Kaua'i.

Then began another battle for Taketa, a battle trying to regain his citizenship so he could return to Hawai'i and his family. It was a long, lonely, and seemingly hopeless battle of 15 years—5,475 lonely days, when each day was 14 to 16 hours of torture and self-recrimination. Why had he been so hasty in renouncing his American citizenship?

Through the efforts of Attorney Wayne Collins of Los Angeles, Taketa was finally allowed to rejoin his family in Hawai'i. He returned June 10, 1961. The following day, June 11, was a festive Kamehameha Day, celebrating Hawai'i's first king's birthday. It was also graduation day for Taketa's son George from Kaua'i High School. Taketa had been unable to see George carry his books to school, bring home a report card, or dress up for a junior or senior prom or banquet. His son had been four when they had separated. And now here he was, graduating from high school!

Taketa had spent 15 of his early childhood years separated from his father and Kaua'i, the place of his birth. He had spent another 15 years of his adult years separated from his wife and children. He had spent four years in a concentration camp.

Now, would he be allowed to live a quiet and normal life on his beloved Kaua'i?

Kalāheo Stockade! Would anyone fifty or a hundred years in the future know that such a camp had existed on Kaua'i? Would tourists passing the lush mountains and valley with such magical, musical names as Papapaholahola, Laauhihaihai and Kalaluanahelehela hear faint echoes of agonized sighs and muted bitterness? Would they even know there had been internee camps located in many states in the United States?

CHAPTER 7

THE HAʻIKŪ CAMP:

The Christmas Tree

When tall, handsome teenager Toraji Yano left Japan for Hawaiʻi without his parents' knowledge but with his elder brother's approval, his chief objective was to learn English quickly.

But in October, 1906, when he walked off the *Mongolia Maru*, there were 264 others like him. Jobs as houseboy or yardman for white families where one was bound to learn English were difficult to obtain. Finally, Toraji and his 19-year-old cousin Masami Tomimatsu left for Kauaʻi to work on a plantation.

Learning English was still his objective, so on Sundays he attended a Christian Church where the services were in English. At first he didn't understand a word that was said, but the flow and cadence of the sermon fascinated him.

Gradually, as he listened to both the Japanese and English sermons, he began to put together what the preachers were saying. Ashamed of his reason for attending the English services, he quit attending in the mornings.

One evening, the English pastor visited him. "Toraji-san, you have stopped coming to our services. Why? We miss you."

Embarrassed, Toraji admitted the truth. "I used to go because I wanted to learn English. But that is not what a church is for. A church talks about God. I'm not interested in God yet. I'm interested in learning English. But it would be selfish of me to go to God's House for my own purposes."

"Ah, but that's where you're wrong, Toraji-san. If you can learn even one word of English each time you come to church, how happy God would be. A church is for fellowship. A church is a place one can accept anything God gives. A church is not only for God; it is for man—for you, for me. May we see you again this Sunday?"

Toraji Yano was to remember that minister all his life. He left Kaua'i for Maui in 1908 and was baptized that year by Rev. Sidney Gulick, the same Rev. Gulick who 33 years later was to serve as Editor Yasutaro Soga's character witness and for whose family the street Kumaji Furuya lived on had been named.

Monday through Saturday, Yano was up at 4:30 a.m. He cooked, ate, and made his lunch; he walked miles to the area he was to work in that day. Then he stumbled home after 5:30. Those were grueling 10-hour days. He ate chiefly dried codfish and rice, and slept on reed mats. One man had been in the islands for 15 years, and he had nothing to show for it. Was this what was going to happen to him too?

Being educated, strong, healthy and outgoing, he decided to quit plantation work. Fortunately, he found work in a store, where he carried out responsibilities over and above what was expected of him. One day, while such jobs were still difficult to obtain, he gained promotion over another man who had been at the store longer. The other man sent Yano a note, saying he wanted to meet him at the graveyard. Yano knew what this meant, but he was husky and he knew *jujitsu*. He was not afraid of fighting, but he didn't want to settle problems that way.

"Why did you take my job" the man accused him at the graveyard.

"I didn't take your job. They offered it to me, and I accepted it."

"But if you hadn't accepted, they'd have offered it to me. I should have that job. I've worked there five years longer than you. I have seniority. You shamed me. You're only a boy, and you can't handle that level of job yet. Let's fight!"

"OK, we can fight, but let's talk first...Now, if we fight, we fight to the finish. One will lose and get hurt and maybe end up in the hospital or even die. The other will win and maybe end up in jail. Definitely, both of us will lose our jobs. Either way, win or lose, we don't have much of a future on this island, do we? Where will you go, if you win?"

The two men sat on gravestones of those who had preceded them to Maui. The cool breeze and the cold tombstones sobered their tempers.

"I wonder who sleeps under this stone? Where did he come from? Why did he come here to Maui? Whom did he leave behind?"

After a few minutes, the other man put out his hand and Yano shook it. The man threw himself on the grass, as if still unhappy. Yano waited. Finally the man got up and shook Yano's hand again and said, "You're right, you know. For a young kid, you think. Maybe I can accept you as my superior because you're mature and intelligent for your age."

Together they walked home, talking about their future in the islands. Would they ever be able to save enough to return to Japan with money to buy a farm of their own?

Later, Yano was told that six of the other man's friends had been hiding in the forest, waiting to fight Yano in case their friend lost. But Yano and the other man became life-long friends after that incident.

After Dec. 7's Pearl Harbor bombing, Yano was investigated at least four times. Once he was asked, "Who do you want to win this war?"

"I want Japan to win, but I don't want the United States to lose. After all this is my adopted country. I've lived here 35 years, in Japan only 18. This is my country by choice. I don't see why the two countries had to engage in war..."

"Nobody's asking you for your opinion!" the interrogator thundered. "Just answer yes or no...all we want are one-word answers."

"But one-word answers cannot provide the whole truth," Yano insisted.

"Silence! Weren't you teaching part-time in a Japanese school? Don't you think learning Japanese language and customs is a hindrance to Americanization ? Surely you can answer those two questions with 'yes' or 'no'."

"One-word answers won't give you the whole picture. I taught Japanese for one hour a day, yes. But we didn't teach obedience to Japan. Why should we? These children are American citizens, unlike us who can't get citizenship. We had these children for one hour, and the English schools had them for six hours a day. Isn't it logical..."

"You talk too much!" The interrogator slammed an open Manila folder shut.

On the day his case was decided, he saw his Red Cross Badge, Japanese song books, his brother's picture taken in Korea, and his wife's brother's photograph in a navy officer's uniform. So these were proof of his disloyalty to the United States!

"Do you want to be interned or go home?" he was teased.

"Of course I want to go home."

"Of course I want to go home," the interrogators mimicked.

Taken to Ha'ikū Camp, he met Shodo Kawamura, the Rev. Shoten Matsubayashi, Shigeru Terada, Tetsuji Hanzawa and other prominent Maui residents. He realized being interned was not a disgrace, for he was among Maui's Japanese community leaders.

During the following weeks and months, others were sent to Honolulu, but Yano was kept at Haʻikū. His responsibility was to pack the items an internee left when he was shipped off and send the carton to the internee's family.

One night Yano and the men heard whimpers and moans, together with exasperated shouts by the MPs. What was taking place?

Then four or five guards opened the door and dragged a man into the barrack. "Anyone know him?"

No one dared answer. After all, no one knew what the man's crime was, and admitting knowing the man before knowing his crime might endanger their lives too.

Then Yano said, "I know him."

"Take him and quiet him down." They left the man shivering with fright. Yano told the man, "I'm Yano of Wailuku. You needn't be afraid here. You're among friends."

The man grabbed him and wouldn't let go. Finally Yano was able to drag him to his own cot and said, "This is my bed. Here's a blanket. Try to rest."

Still the man trembled, so Yano sat by him until the man fell asleep. In the morning, Yano learned that the terrified man was the third strongest sumo wrestler in his district. His crime: a light had been visible in one of his windows. There was a huge mango tree shading the house, making the light invisible to enemy planes or ships, but an overzealous warden had "carried out his duty."

Three days later, the man was released.

One day, as kitchen helper, Yano came across a bag of spoiled sweet potatoes in the storeroom. While dumping the contents into a refuse drum, he found two of the potatoes looked quite good. He requested and received permission to take the two potatoes to his barrack.

He sliced off the rotted portion and put the potatoes in a basin filled with a quarter-inch of water. Soon the potatoes sprouted eyes. Day by day, Yano and his barrack mates examined the plants and urged them to grow. Then, when the vines began to form, Yano got two pieces of wood and nailed them into a cross, then to a heavy base. He lovingly tied the shoots to the cross, and in a month he had a Christmas Tree!

Next, all the men cooperated in saving tin foil from cigarette packs. They made decorations from the foil—tiny stars, balls, triangles, even angels—which they attached as ornaments to their Christmas tree.

One day a senior official passed by the barrack, saw the tree, and asked, "Why do you have a Christmas tree? And this is June..."

"Because I'm a Christian, and we can have the spirit of Christmas anytime in the year..."

"But you're Japanese. You must be Buddhists. I hear loud pray-ing from the barracks..."

"Oh, that's Rev. Matsubayashi. He's a Buddhist but I'm a Christian. Baptized in 1908. 34 years ago. Before you were born."

"I'm glad to hear that. I'm a Christian too. Again we live in a time when I'm a guard and you're the enemy. But I know you Japanese in Hawai'i are not our real enemy. You're only a symbol of the enemy because you happen to have Japanese blood. Please forgive me if I have to give you unpleasant orders."

"That's OK. You have your duty as Army officers. We hold nothing against you or the other guards personally. Keeping us here is not your decision. Some of us are frustrated at not being able to be useful people, especially in the prime of our lives. But most of us are not bitter. Depressed, yes. But we have discussed among ourselves the reasons for our being interned. We are the scapegoats. We are willing to be that if the other Japanese can live normally."

Within a few months, Yano was quietly paroled.

And Ha'ikū Camp, an unhappy experience for many, was only another opportunity for Yano to express his love and faith in Christ.

His baptism, in 1908, had been the most rewarding, the most meaningful act in his life; he believed fully and deeply in Christ's love and tried to follow in His footsteps.

The minister in Kauaʻi, who had taught him a few words and sentences in English so many years ago, had taught him more than that. He had given Yano the desire and the ability to love others.

CHAPTER 8

THE SHIP AND TRAIN RIDE:

Locked In!

The internees who boarded the *U.S.S. Ulysses Grant* on February 20, 1942, staggered down, down, down three flights below the main deck. Some could hardly manage the steep stairs even without the stuffed duffel bags. Young men like Shigeo Shigenaga and Rev. Kenjitsu Tsuha helped the older and weaker by tying two duffel bags and swinging one pair over each shoulder.

The *Grant* was escorted by two destroyers. In all, about eight ships, including the *Lurline* and the *Pierce*, formed a convoy which zigzagged its way to San Francisco. There were no portholes for they were below sea-level, no books or magazines, and only a dim light, but ventilation was good.

What made the internees miserable was that they were locked, eight or ten in a room, for three hours at a time. At the end of three hours the door was unlocked and a guard escorted the men to a makeshift oil barrel latrine. Then it was back to the locked room. It was continued days of humiliation and suffering, especially for those with bladder problems. Sometimes the men pounded on the door, begging to be allowed to use the toilet. "I must go…I must go now," they pleaded, but the guards ignored the pounding. Later groups of internees did not have to suffer this indignity, but for the first contingent of Japanese internees sent to the Mainland, there was tight regimentation and no exceptions were allowed.

During those days and nights of desperation, as "accidents" happened, the men remembered the nights at Sand Island with nostalgia. At Sand Island the moon had been full and clear. At Sand Island one could see sparkling stars…yes, the stars really did sparkle and twinkle, as in nursery rhymes. The black-and-white landscape in the bright moonlight had been like a *sumi-e*, a black-ink painting. Often some of the men had gone to the latrine at night, calling out "Prisoner" or "Poisoner" or even "Piss-oner" to the guard, simply to admire the beauty of the night. Here, on the ship, they could hardly move without getting in someone's way, and the smell was getting unbearable.

As the men recalled the events of the past few months, they realized that everything was relative. When they had been at Sand Island, they had hated its monotony and prison-like atmosphere. Now they cherished the memory of its serenity, its peacefulness.When they had been at the Immigration Station, they had complained over the stuffiness of the overpacked room with people lying all over the floor and with only two toilets for the 170 men. Now they realized what a luxury even one toilet was, provided it was accessible.

As the *U.S.S. Grant* cautiously snaked its way across the Pacific, watchful for signs of Japanese submarines, the internees passed the time in different ways.

Some saved orange peels and divided these into dime-sized pieces. With these they played go, a game similar to chess, using the orange rind to represent black stones and the white pulp as white stones. Others engaged in storytelling: travel or business adventures, early immigrant experiences, and the legends and lore of Japan.

One night, on the way to dinner, Kumaji Furuya noticed a sailor polishing his shoes. He nudged his friend. They looked at the other sailors. All had an air of anticipation about them.

What exhilaration there was back in the room that night. They were nearing land. Else why would the sailors be looking so neat?

The memory of ten days and nights of hardship evaporated. They looked at each other fondly. Never, not even at home, had ten persons lived so closely, so intimately with others. They felt like double sets of quintuplets who had shared the same dark womb, the same umbilical cord. For ten days they had hated each other's smell, voice, sight, accidental touch, mannerisms. But now that the end was in sight, they looked at each other with affection, forgetting the smell of urine, the sight of bearded and drawn faces, the throb of engines directly below them night and day, the feel of suffocation in a locked room below sea level. They had woven a tight bond of togetherness and they were to be more than "brothers" for a long time to come.

The crisp fresh air at San Francisco, where the *Grant* docked at 3:30 p.m. on March 1, was invigorating. The Golden Gate, which had been visible for a few minutes as the fog lifted tantalizingly, shimmered as the late afternoon sun pierced the light mist. Although the internees were the last to walk off the ship, having to remain on board for almost two hours, they had no complaint. They were near land, and the land was beautiful.

Transferred into small tugboats, they sailed past Oakland, Berkeley and Richmond to Angel Island, which housed the Quarantine Station. Some of the men had never seen San Francisco, and this glimpse of the city and its environs reminded them of the misty hills of Japan. And, as the minutes ticked away, it grew dark and a million lights shone in the distance. After months of blacked-out Hawai'i, it seemed like a fairyland.

The men did not mind being photographed, fingerprinted, and examined in the nude for "infectious diseases." This took from 9 p.m. to 6 a.m. and it was cold, a damp clinging cold. After their clothes and duffel bags had been examined, they were each given two blankets and told to go upstairs to rest. It seemed like they were back at the Immigration Station in Honolulu, but now when they took a hot shower, used the toilet, or did their laundry, these simple acts were indeed luxuries.

Angel Island was a continuation of the fairyland that was called San Francisco. Birds welcomed them in the morning, and cherry and acacia trees bloomed in pink and white glory. Such beauty, after ten days in the confining walls of the ship's hold, made them drunk with joy.

But how many tears of frustration, of fear, of sorrow must have fallen at this Station! The building, old and deteriorating, had been used to receive Oriental immigrants for some 75 years. First had come the Chinese to build railroads. Then Japanese immigrants had been encouraged to take the place of the resented industrious Chinese. Gradually they too posed a danger and threat as they set their roots in the soil. To make sure the Japanese would not remain in this country too long, laws were passed, such laws as that Japanese aliens could not own land, marry Caucasians or become naturalized citizens. But when the immigrants first landed, who cared to own land here, marry a hairy "white," or become an

American citizen? Their only goal was to save money and return to Japan.

Today, in March 1942, the Station was packed solid. Like the Immigration Station in Honolulu, this one had three-tiered bed-shelves lining the walls. Men also slept on their blankets on the floor. They were so crowded, 140 to a room, that they could hardly move.

Four men went as representatives to an official and protested the overcrowding. The official shrugged his shoulders. The Army had sent too many internees at one time. What could he do? There was no outside housing during these war years, and anyway the Japanese enemy aliens needed protection from thoughtless outsiders. Their stay here would be short—only a few days, or until train transportation could be provided. The official expressed sympathy, but he could do nothing to ease the overcrowding. The internees understood and had to accept the conditions since there were no other alternatives.

But they decided to do something about the food. Some men volunteered to help in the messhall. Masao Sakamoto went into the kitchen and cooked rice the way the Japanese liked it—soft and sticky. He used ingredients in the kitchen to make pseudo-Oriental food. Others went in and made the messhall shine. The military cooks were happy to have help; the internees were happy to have food cooked to their liking; the volunteers got an extra serving at each meal.

The men were allowed to walk the grounds around the dorm for half an hour three times a day. They exercised loudly and joyfully. The atmosphere was almost like that of a Japanese business firm's retreat or country hostel.

To make conditions even more pleasant, a thoughtful Catholic father brought newspapers and magazines for the Italian internees. It was through these newspapers that the Hawai'i internees first learned about the mass evacuation of West Coast Japanese to temporary camps somewhere inland. In fact, President Franklin D. Roosevelt had signed

Executive order 9066 on February 19, 1942, the day before they boarded the *Grant* to be shipped to the Mainland. The Order made it possible to remove all Japanese from borders of the West Coast, even though
it did not pinpoint the Japanese specifically.

It was at Angel Island that the Hawai'i internees met a tattooed 50-
year-old Japanese. As youngsters, Japanese are usually told never to
associate with gamblers or with members of a gang called *yakuza*.
Like the mafia, members of one *yakuza* are said to gang-war with
members of another *yakuza*, if that *yakuza* encroached on the first
yakuza's territory. Children were told to keep away from tattooed
men or men with a baby finger missing.

But here was a tattooed man in their midst, without a gang to
belong to. At first he spoke chiefly in monosyllables, but gradually he
warmed to the Hawai'i Japanese. He told them he had jumped ship
over 20 years ago and had lived in the U.S. ever since. He had never
married, never applied for a social security card, driver's license, welfare or anything that required official attention and approval. Only
because he had a Japanese face and name and was on the West Coast
had he finally been netted for questioning. The Hawai'i Japanese
were grateful to this man for he provided some of them cigarettes,
postcards and stamps.

On the fifth day at the Immigration Station, the men were all
assembled on the exercise grounds. An announcement was made that
they were to go to a camp elsewhere.

"We want the older and weaker of you to step forward," the
official said.

"I think you're going to get the sleeping cars," the younger ones said.
"I don't know how long we're going to ride, but you couldn't sit up
overnight. It would be too hard on you."

It was only after they were loaded on freight trains converted
into passenger cars that they found the older and the frail were in a
car which didn't have windows with glass—only meshed wire

installed temporarily—and which lacked doors. The elderly and the ill had been put in that car because they were not strong or agile enough to slip to freedom through the guards, placed at both ends of the car.

Later trainloads of internees rode in luxury, with wide seats, ice water and three meals a day. But for those going to Camp McCoy in Wisconsin on March 6, 1942, the converted train was old, slow and sooty. Forty of them were sardined into each car, and they sat for four days and three nights with only one blanket each to keep warm in the cold March weather. Soot, when the train passed through a tunnel, blackened hair and faces, until they all looked more or less alike.

At large stations they were told to lower the shades and to keep to one's seat, as one never knew what people might do to the internees. But at the stations people looked at them curiously and sympathetically, and at one station a group of women identified as "American Friends" handed them some packages. In them they found dried fruit and candy. The guards confiscated the packages, saying they could be poisoned. But later they were seen eating the candy themselves.

Now the men remembered the ship with nostalgia. On it they could lie down. It was torture, sitting up for so many days and nights. Their bodies ached. When would they reach their destination? They asked an Army doctor, but he shook his head.

On a later train, Matsujiro Otani, a Honolulu millionaire businessman, rode in the hot July sun through shimmering desert. When the train stopped at Phoenix, Arizona, the men looked out. There it was, a huge, plump, ice-cold watermelon, marked 30¢! The men eyed the watermelon longingly, but they didn't have 30¢ among them. Not only that, the guard would not have allowed them to get off the train.

They were all silent, but Matsutaro Shimizu, a fisherman who helped Otani because he was ill, said, "Maybe we'll have ice cream for lunch."

They did have ice cream for dessert. It was delicious, but it left them even more hot and thirsty. They vowed that when they returned to Hawai'i, if they were allowed to do so, they would gorge themselves on ice-cold watermelon.

It was George Hoshida, who left Hawai'i on May 23, 1942, who witnessed a scene he would never forget. George had lived 30 of his 34 years in Hawai'i. He was a salesman and part-time *judo* instructor, and *judo*, George was told by Army interrogators, was a martial art that "taught obedience" to Japan. Being a *judo* instructor was "proof of potential undersirability as a free individual resident."

Always in George's mind was the image of his eight-year-old daughter, Taeko, paralyzed in one half of her body, blind and mute. It was five years since she had convulsions which twisted her with pain into a curled shrimp. He wondered how his wife was managing to care for Taeko when there were two younger children, one seven and one only two years old. It had been difficult enough, even with him at home. Now she was pregnant, expecting a baby in October. There was no salary to pay for the mortgage on their home, and no one to turn Taeko on her bed.

Suddenly the train slowed as it entered a railroad yard. Signs indicated this was Salt Lake City. The train rumbled back, then forward, then back again as one car was unhooked and another attached. Then the train came parallel to another passenger train doing the same thing.

The Hawai'i internees looked out the window. Oh, they were Japanese, those people in the next train! They looked at each other and waved, like old friends long separated. They both knew what it meant to be Japanese in early 1942, and the fact that they were evacuees or internees created an instant bond of kinship. There were women and children on the train, with boxes and packages piled high, so the Hawai'i Japanese identified them as Mainland relocatees being sent to some WRA camp.

When next Hoshida saw the same train, the people were disembarking with their baggage and moving toward another train. But, Hoshida saw, there were two people left, a man of about 50 and a boy of about 20. At that moment the boy's body was contracted in horrible distortion, his face pale and perspiring. His fists were clenched and he had the same shrimp-like position Hoshida's daughter used to struggle into when she was in convulsions. The father, standing by the boy, had his fists clenched and his back arched, almost as if he too were in convulsions. Then, as Hoshida watched in agony and sympathy, the boy's body relaxed and straightened, the facial muscles loosened, the fists unclenched, and the boy made a movement to sit up. The father pulled a towel from a coat pocket, wiped the boy's face tenderly, smoothed his hair, held his hand and helped him up. He held the boy for a brief moment, then the two, gathering some boxes, walked off the train to join the others. A guard, standing close by, offered to help but he was ignored.

"Taeko, my daughter, what will happen to her?" Hoshida wrote in his diary that day. "Will she ever reach this boy's age? But this boy can walk. This boy can see. Taeko cannot walk, she cannot talk, she cannot see. Would it have been better if she had died during the car accident? She was only three months old then. She wouldn't have known all that pain. No…no, today she's eight, and she's had five rather good years. She recognizes my voice, my wife's voice. She is a person, a human being. She presses my hand when I speak to her. She smiles and even gurgles when the other children play with her. Of course she shouldn't have died. Taeko, how I wish I could have remained home with you. The U.S. government, the FBI, wants to punish me for being an alien Japanese in the U.S., for teaching judo part-time. Don't they realize that seeing you day after day was punishment enough? That I curse the day the accident happened? That I tell myself that if I had been two minutes late or two minutes early in making that turn into our yard, that truck wouldn't have hit us and maimed us? Is it I that the government is punishing, or is it my wife and you, Taeko, and the other children? How can I, with a paralyzed daughter, two young children, and a pregnant wife be a threat to a nation? Where would I have the time, the energy, the skill, when I had to spend all my spare time at home with you, Taeko?"

A few months after Hoshida was interned, Taeko had to be taken to Waimanu Home on Oʻahu by her uncle. There she died, died without being able to ask, "What happened to my mother? My father? Why don't I hear their voices or feel them holding my hand anymore? To whom do these strange, harsh, impatient voices belong? Daddy? Mommy? What happened?"

It was March 9 in Wisconsin. Soft fluffy snow covered rooftops, bushes and ground. It rested lightly on branches of trees and made little mounds on fence posts. Icicles hung from eaves. Two weeks ago there had been a blizzard and the mercury had plunged to 15 degrees below zero. But today it was a gentle, silent white world.

In this serene peacefulness a line of decrepit trains clanked and clattered into the station, spouting clouds of black smoke, then expired with a giant yawn and exhausted hisses.

Officials at Camp McCoy had been alerted that the Hawaiʻi Japanese internees were coming. Undoubtedly envisioning dangerous fifth columnists who had been instrumental in the devastation of Pearl Harbor, the camp commander had 30 steel-helmeted, battle-ready soldiers at the station, bayonets poised for action.

The last car with the frail and elderly was unloaded first. Forty of the internees stumbled out. All wore heavy long GI overcoats which had been issued to them before they left Hawaiʻi, but underneath some wore flimsy aloha shirts and lightweight trousers suitable only for Hawaiian weather.

They shivered as the cold penetrated the overcoat, and they stretched shoulders, arms and legs to exercise the stiffness and exhaustion out of their bodies. Yet they touched the soft snow, piled high along the hedges, almost in delight, as they viewed the quiet beauty surrounding them. They looked old, dried up, mummified, because they drooped with fatigue and weariness and were covered with soot, yet at the same time they looked like little children, lifting a finger of snow in wonderment and admiring its delicate beauty.

Unknown to them, the camp commander must have issued an order, for the bayoneted soldiers disappeared. By the time the last train car had been emptied, all that could be seen were many undersized bodies in oversized overcoats lining up as usual for the next abrupt command.

CHAPTER 9

CAMP McCOY:

BANZAI! Col. Rogers, Sir!

It was almost dark and biting cold when Kumaji Furuya, Dr. Miyamoto, Rev. Tsuha and others of the first contingent of Hawai'i internees reached Camp McCoy, Wisconsin, on Mary 9. The camp served as Civilian Conservation Corps barracks during the depression years in the early 1930s. There were rolling hills, pine and oak groves, and a huge military training area within its 20,000 acres. Farmhouses, barns and silos dotted the approach to the camp.

There were about a hundred European nationals already there, including Catholic priests, engineers, musicians and professors of languages. Most of the men were well educated professionals who had been born in the wrong countries: Germany, Italy and Hungary.

The exhausted Hawai'i men found they could take a hot shower after the sooty, bone-tiring trip. The four barracks had two stoves roaring in each of the barracks. Later they found that it was a "drifter" from Oregon, an itinerant who had worked on the railroad and picked fruit on farms in many states who had attended to the boiler room and provided wood for the eight stoves. He did not know any of the Hawai'i men, yet he had worked hard to make their entry into Camp McCoy comfortable. The Hawai'i internees compared him to six well-dressed Japanese international businessmen from Seattle; they found the "drifter" sincere, humble and considerate.

Each internee was issued three blankets, two sheets, a pillow and a pillow-case. For the first time since being picked up on Dec. 7, the men slept between clean sheets; they slept well, after the exhausting three-night, four-day train ride.

Soon after their arrival a new commander was assigned to the camp. He was Lt. Col. Horace Ivan Rogers, a Detroit lawyer in civilian life.

"Gentlemen," he addressed them, "I welcome you to Camp McCoy. I want you to know that we respect you, for you are not criminals. You are not being held for acts committed against our nation. We are merely detaining you, who are enemy aliens, for reasons of our own. If you have problems or concerns, please have your representative make an appointment with me and I shall try to be of service to you."

Rogers realized how traumatic the change in weather could be for these men coming from Hawai'i, especially dressed as they were, for one day he announced that roll call would be at 9 p.m. in the barracks, just before lights were to be turned off. The men were astonished, especially since he often came into each barrack alone, leaving two guards outside. He nodded to each man as he clicked his hand counter. At this moment, the opportunity was there for anyone to approach him with any complaint. The men did not know it, but Col. Rogers had direct access to the Chief of Intelligence in Washington, D.C.

When Rogers entered, the men sat deferentially on their knees, Japanese fashion, and bowed, returning his greetings. First they had thought he was too familiar and friendly for a military officer, but in a few days that feeling turned to deep respect.

Because he was so kind, Masao Sakamoto, the chef, asked him if they could celebrate Hanamatsuri or Prince Siddharta Day on April 8. This day is to Buddhists what Christmas is to Christians. Rogers agreed, but asked that he be allowed to attend the festivities.

Rev. Hakuai Oda, an expert in the art of making artificial flowers and in floral arrangement, made cherry blossoms by dyeing toilet tissue in diluted beet juice and fashioning pink petals. He attached these to a dry oak tree branch. The result looked almost like a real cherry tree. And like a real tree, petals occasionally fell, as if to symbolize the passing of time and the transience of life.

Rev. Rien Takahashi fashioned the figure of a newborn Prince Siddharta out of a large carrot. The legend is that the Prince was born from the right side of Queen Maya, stepped several feet forward, pointed to Heaven and Earth and announced, "Between Heaven and Earth, I alone am to be revered."

Thirty priests, led by Rev. Ninryo Nago with his flowing white beard, participated in the service.

Co. Rogers, who had donated cake and fruit for the occasion, got up and addressed them. "Gentlemen," he began. It was as if an invisible cloak of gentlemenness had enveloped each of them, and their affection for this officer shone in their faces. If he thought they were gentlemen, they would be gentlemen. They would not, could not, let this man down.

The days passed. The internees seemed contented enough, as they stumbled to the dining room in other people's footsteps. Food was plentiful, and, with volunteers in the kitchen, tasty enough. The men ate and slept, slept and ate. They obeyed passively and meekly any and all commands. They looked, in their overcoats, like bulky silk cocoons...without personality, without individuality.

To the perceptive physician's eyes of Dr. Kazuo Miyamoto the men looked like zombies. "Col. Rogers," he reported, "the men are deteriorating both physically and mentally. These men were leaders in their community. They were always active. They need to be involved, even in their camp community."

Col. Rogers agreed. "Any ideas?"

Together they discussed possible activities. As a result, Rogers brought in used gloves, balls and bats for the young and athletic. Teams were formed and these challenged one another, working toward a camp championship. Now the younger men ignored the cold weather, and came back to the barracks eyes alert, faces ruddy, and voices ringed with laughter and triumph.

The older men liked to polish stones they found. Pebbles from the age of lava and glaciers made beautiful semi-precious jewelry. Rogers had three truckloads of stones dredged from the lake bottom brought to the camp. The men eagerly sought certain pieces; in their minds they could see the result of shaping and polishing.

Then there was a broadcast team, consisting of Shoichi Asami, Dr. Tokue Takahashi and Dr. Kazuo Miyamoto. The three would read the English papers—the camp subscribed to the *New York Times*, *Chicago Tribune*, and others—then summarized the news into Japanese. Asami gave news of home, gleaned from letters received from the internees and from island newspapers; Takahashi reported war news; and Miyamoto selected pertinent national news. The one-and-a-half hour broadcast spurred many discussions among the men.

One night, as spring limped in after a long winter, Col. Rogers entered their barracks. It was already 10 p.m., an hour after lights had to be off. Some men were asleep. Those awake wondered what they had done wrong, or whether they were to be moved in the middle of a cold winter night.

"Gentlemen, have you ever seen the Northern Lights?" the Colonel asked.

"The what?"

"The Northern Lights," he repeated, pointing to the stars outside.

"Yes, every night. When we were at Sand Island," they replied, thinking he meant stars.

"Why don't you put on your shoes and overcoat and come outside?" he suggested.

Some of the men were suspicious; perhaps they were going to be transferred again. Remembering the days when they didn't even have a handkerchief, they changed into a suit and stuffed belongings into a duffel bag before donning their overcoats and walking outside.

The world around them was still, frosty—a black and white picture. But as they stood, stamping because of the cold, a change came over the sky. It shone several shades of silver, a very pale blue, pale green, and a hint of lavender and pink. It looked as if God had suddenly turned on a million volts of pastel-colored lightning for some sort of celebration.

Few of the men had ever heard of an aurora borealis before. Its delicate beauty and grandeur was such that it seemed almost supernatural. Because it was unexpected, it was doubly dazzling in its majesty. They loved it and they loved Col. Rogers for allowing them to share in this phenomenon.

Days and weeks—including spring—came and went. The men still looked ragged as they waited anxiously for their suitcases and for their $50, held up somewhere. Finally, in May, just as the warm season began, the winter clothes arrived, too late to use until the following winter. But the men felt closer to home with the arrival of their clothes, for each item was numbered by hand by a family member. The $50 they never received!

But in May, they were told they could receive up to $30 a month from home. What a great day that was! The last time Kumaji Furuya had fingered cash was when Sho Tominaga of *Samoa* gave twenty of them a dollar each. Furuya remembered that day. He had looked longingly at all the items that could be purchased for a dollar. Again and again he had mentally selected and added his purchases. His final decision:[3] 20¢ airmail stamps, 13¢ soap, 10¢ toothpowder, 6¢ cup, 5¢ cough-drops, 5¢ candy and l¢ match.

Also, in May, they received letters, some months old. Someone even received a telegram from Japan! The men were exuberant. Now they were part of civilization again! They could be in touch with their families!

Then, a few weeks later, the men were informed they were to report to a camp further south. Camp McCoy was to be the training grounds for the 100th Infantry, a battalion made up of Hawai'i National Guard members and volunteers into the Army.

When the Camp McCoy internees left Wisconsin, they were told only that they were being moved south about 800 miles. This time it was a short 24-hour ride, as compared to the exhausting 4-day, 3-night ride from San Francisco to Wisconsin. The men were not guarded every minute; in fact, they had to make their own sandwiches.

When it was announced that they would soon be at the train station, they looked out the window to see a plateau with huge groves of oak trees. They learned the elevation was 2,000 feet above sea level, and the town close by was Tullahoma, Tennessee, close to Georgia and Alabama. These three states were not in the internees' travel vocabulary, like California and New York.

Camp Forrest, their destination, was two miles away from the train station, and large enough to accommodate 40,000 troops. As the men were taken to their quarters, they noticed that there were both black and white troops there, but they were in separate units. And now here was a yellow unit, an unarmed unit, yet this unit was surrounded by barbed wire, watch towers, guards and dogs!

Accommodations for the internees had just been completed. The huts, built for five men each, were of knotty pine. The boards were warped and did not fit well together. Chill air filtered in through cracks, but the men were not seriously disturbed. They knew that with hammer, nails and scraps of lumber such defects could easily be remedied.

The men lined up for army cots, thin mattresses, pillows and sheets. By this time most of them could quickly set up a cot, unlike as at Sand Island. Each one who finished early helped another.

Food at Camp Forrest was good and plentiful. They could even have all the sugar they wanted. The first night, seeing there was more sugar than would be needed, some of the men ladled sugar into clean paper napkins for use in the future. But the next day they saw the sugar bowls had been refilled. Finally, reassured, they returned the "borrowed" sugar back into the sugar bowl. "We're lucky," they commented. "I understand back home sugar is rationed."

Unlike at Sand Island and Camp McCoy, lights at Camp Forrest could be on till 11 p.m. and they could sleep till 7 a.m. The men were more contented than they admitted, especially since they had self-rule, attended classes, could engage in hobbies, and could receive money and letters from home. Now, just as they had collected shells and coral at Sand Island to occupy their time, they turned their attention to collecting fossils. It became a consuming desire to find a fossil and make it into a watch fob. The men seemed to lose their individualism in their desire to have what the others had, in this case, a watch fob.

This desire related to clothing too. At Wisconsin, they had all worn Army woolen trousers and Mackinow coats, originally purchased in the 1930s for Civilian Conservation Corp youth. In Tennessee the woolens were taken away and the men were issued green shirts and pants. Strangely, the clothes fit. It was as if the uniforms had been made especially for them.

Later they learned why. A shipment of these uniforms had been made especially for Philippine scouts to use in jungle warfare. But with the fall of Manila to the Japanese, the American ship had returned to the Mainland with the uniforms still in the hold. Some bright quartermaster must have seen the size of the uniforms, realized they were too small for American soldiers, and put his memory of Japanese internees to good use by getting uniforms and men together.

The uniforms were a bright green when first issued, but under the Tennessee summer sun turned to a mottled greenish tan. Soon an internee asked the supply officer for some green dye. One day this ingenious internee appeared in a bright green uniform.

How nice he looked! He stood out from the rest of the men in their faded uniforms. The others wanted to know how he had done it. Within a few weeks almost everyone appeared in bright green again. Now the internee in the faded uniform stood out in that section of the camp.

Furuya remembered how he used to tell his wife not to copy women who wore different fashions as the styles changed—from long hemlines to shorter hemlines, from no sleeves to puff sleeves to raglan sleeves to peplum sleeves. It was "monkey see, monkey do," he told her. "Don't be a copycat. Be yourself. Wear fashions that suit you."

And now here he was, anxious to have his uniform dyed green, just like the others. He was forgetting about ideas, commitments. What had happened to him in just six months? How had he changed so? What had made a community leader and businessman overwhelmingly concerned about the color of his clothes ? Was this what brainwashing meant? Or did this happen to all incarcerated men, no matter how pleasantly incarcerated they were? He almost chose not to dye his uniform, in protest, but his desire for a fresh green shirt and trousers overcame his desire not to give in to conformity.

During the hot days that began in June, the men gathered on benches set in oak groves. These were the coolest spots available, and they spent their time reminiscing about the past and wondering about the future.

With the heat came the flies. They buzzed on the food, in the huts, under the trees, everywhere. Finally the men organized a fly brigade, since they didn't have any spray to control the insects. Armed with folded news-papers the brigade systematically battled the flies as if they were the enemy.

"Here, take this!" A fly lay with tiny legs moving feebly.

"Hah! Three at a time!"

"You are the enemy and you must die!"

"Whom are you killing, the American soldiers or the Japanese soldiers? Which side is the enemy?"

The swatter looked surprised. "Why...the enemy is the enemy. The ones we're supposed to hate."

"The Americans have us locked up in this camp. Behind barbed wire. With machine guns pointed at us. Are they the enemy?"

"How can the Americans be the enemy? My wife is an American. Some of my brothers and sisters are Americans. My friends and children are Americans. Can my children, my relatives and friends be the enemy? Sure, we're in camps, but are we behind bars like in a real prison? Are we starved? Tortured? Didn't the Americans take care of Bishop Kuchiba when he had appendicitis? I don't like being interned, but that is not saying the Americans are the enemy."

"The Japanese soldiers then? Are the Japanese military the enemy, since they force the common people to engage in war?"

"How can the Japanese be my enemy when I'm Japanese myself? I was born there. Japan is still my country since I can't ever be an American citizen. How can the people of my country be my enemy?"

"Who, then? You said you were killing the enemy. Who is this enemy?"

"The enemy," the man answered, swatting another batch of flies, "is someone I don't know, haven't seen, and whose face I can't imagine. He doesn't have human characteristics. If he's a human being, someone with parents who worry over him, grand-parents who watched him grow, children who wait for him to return, and a dog that licks his hand and face, how can I hate him enough to kill him?"

"In other words, then, an enemy is not a person. It is just a word, an idea..."

"I suppose so. The enemy is faceless. Until our government puts the word and people together, and they become one. The 'idea' of an enemy merges with the man through propaganda in the newspapers and on radio. A man we have never seen whose background we don't know about is the enemy."

"This is too complicated. Let's just kill flies. They're insects, not the enemy."

With the transfer of internees from Col. Rogers of Camp McCoy to Capt. Laemmle of Camp Forrest completed, Rogers was to return to Wisconsin and to other duties.

On the day he was to leave, the Hawai'i internees gathered in front of the dining hall. Rogers shook each man's hand, wishing him well. Then, as he said his final goodbye, the internees' voices resounded in a spontaneous cheer, "Horace Rogers, *Banzai! Banzai! Banzai!*" This was the greatest gift the men could give him, for *banzais* were at one time restricted for the emperor. Perhaps it was the first and only time prisoners incarcerated in an enemy camp cheered and showed their esteem and respect for their jailor. *Banzai!* I hope you live ten thousand years! The men were acclaiming and honoring the spirit shown by Rogers: his fairness, his understanding, his kindness, the humaneness with which he had administered his camp.

Banzai! What did it matter that Rogers was Caucasian and they Japanese enemy aliens? His words, his actions were not influenced by ethnic or national considerations. He had ignored race and position during a critical period of suspicion and distrust. He was a man, and he had treated them as fellow-men.

Banzai! Rogers, Sir!

CHAPTER 10

FORT SILL:

Death of a Barber

Another contingent of Hawai'i's internees, chiefly from the outer islands, was sent to Fort Sill, Oklahoma.

When George Hoshida reached San Antonio, Texas, at 8 a.m. on June 8, 1942, the first object to really catch his attention was a statue of an Indian with a bow and arrow, high atop the dome of a building. The sun's rays formed a yellow-gold halo around the shining head. It seemed as if Jesus was an Indian, welcoming an ethnic group that resembled him.

The trucks that picked up the internees at the San Antonio train station each had two armed guards; the guards seemed puzzled by the islanders' pidgin English. On the other hand, the internees listened to the Texas drawl and nudged each other. "Funny kine way they talk, yeh?" they whispered. "You can unnerstan um...?"

When George saw the cool-looking cement building with the sign "Fort Sam Houston," he was relieved. There were shady trees, flower gardens and green grass. A sprinkler misted the air. It was already 110 degrees in the truck, and the men couldn't wait to get off.

But instead of stopping, the trucks rumbled on. And after a few more miles, there it was—their camp. There was no mistaking it this time.

"Fort Sam Houston Internment Camp" was the sign that greeted them. The omnipresent barbed wire fences were there, as if the hot and barren desert itself were not an impenetrable barrier. There were no trees, flowers or grass. The barracks were tents. It was 10 a.m. and already heat waves enveloped them. What would it be like at noon?

They soon found out, for it took over an hour to be assigned to a tent.

About 300 internees were already there; half of them looked Japanese, but when spoken to, they merely smiled and nodded, making indistinguishable sounds. Their clothes had extra large POW letters painted on back and knees. Soon the Hawai'i men learned that these were Alaskan Eskimos.

Fort Sam Houston was burning hot. The tents did not shield the men from the merciless sun, so the men took refuge in shower stalls, latrines and laundry area, which were slightly cooler. Then the temperature dropped at night. Coming from Hawai'i, the men considered the weather their greatest enemy.

Fortunately, after nine days, the men were transferred to Lordsburg, New Mexico. Lordsburg was hot too, but at night it was cool and even during the day it was a dry hot.

When they had reached the train station, some of the trucks that were supposed to pick them up were not there. It was the hottest time of day, and some of the men had to walk two miles, four abreast. They plodded and stumbled, but they kept moving, for to be left in the desert would mean dehydration and heat stroke. They could also be shot for attempting to escape.

"Why didn't I keep my mouth shut?" George Hoshida scolded himself, putting one foot in front of another with great effort. "If only I had kept quiet when the examiners told me judo was pro-Japanese training! Why did I have to argue that judo in itself is not pro-Japanese or pro-any nationality? Why didn't I just nod and say, 'Yes, sir, yes, sir'?"

But George realized that, given the same circumstances, he would still try to explain that judo or any other martial arts is in itself not nationalistic.

He thought back to a time he could hardly remember, back in 1912, when he was four. His father Yotaro had come to Hawai'i in 1907, when his wife Eno had been pregnant with George. He had also left three other children in Japan. Yotaro had worked hard and hoarded every penny, but in five years all he had saved was enough for his wife Eno and two of the four children. After much discussion in George's grandfather's home, it was decided that the oldest and the youngest would get to emigrate to Hawai'i.

George had been four. Since then he had lived 30 years in Hawai'i, but he always had to call himself an alien. It was strange, for when he looked into a mirror, he saw an American, not a Japanese citizen!

Another contingent of 166 Hawai'i internees reached Fort Sill, Oklahoma. For Otokichi Ozaki, it was his fifth time to be stripped naked and eighth time to be examined for contraband. Everything written in Japanese, even a sheet of poetry, was confiscated.

The next day, this Hawai'i group met the internees from Panama. They had been chiefly barbers and stonecrafters in that country. "In the U.S., the Chinese are supposed to become cooks and laundrymen. The

Japanese are to be farmers and gardeners, even if they have college degrees. In Panama, Japanese are accepted as barbers and stonecrafters," they explained. "If we tried to enter another field, there would be resentment. Of course some of our children succeed, just as some of your children succeed here in the U.S."

Also at Fort Sill were people who had been famous names to the Hawai'i people. There was Ichiro Matsudaira from Japan's royal family. There was Michio Ito, a famous dancer who had been stranded in New York. There was Yajiro Noda, the millionaire cotton king.

Others were there from Peru, Bolivia and Nicaragua. They spoke Spanish among themselves, Japanese to the others.

The Fort Sill internees talked about what had happened on *Ten chosetsu*, the Emperor's birthday. At Camp Forrest, the men had had fried eggs, sunny side up, which resembled a Japanese flag. Here at Fort Sill, the men from the different countries had gathered together, with permission, to celebrate the event.

"We did the *banzai* on April 29 not three times but about twenty times," Chikuma explained. The powerful voices of these usually shy and quiet men had astounded the guards. The internees themselves felt more relaxed after having yelled at the top of their voices in a permitted act, each internee indistinguishable one from the other. They had roared "*Banzai! Banzai! Banzai!*" and thundered out their frustra-tion, their bitterness, their misery and cleansed their soul for the days to follow.

One early twilight, Otokichi Ozaki, poet-philosopher-teacher by trade, looked up and saw a swirl of birds flying in a long neat V across the sky. The birds followed a leader, flying straight when the lead bird did so, swerving in S formation when the leader led in this design. It was a beautiful sight, but it made the men watching the birds realize that the birds were followers, always going where the lead bird went. They were followers, like sheep, or like the internees. The internees hesitated to question, originate or deviate for they could be denied privileges. One sold his soul for the privilege of a meal three times a day, a cot in an uncomfortable tent, and human companionship. When, at what moment, when they were supposed to be community leaders, had they reconciled themselves to accept meekly, without even a twinge of resentment? It was a disquieting thought.

Of course some still served as leaders, such men as Dr. Takahashi and Dr. Miyamoto. But because many of the men didn't or couldn't speak English well, they were forced to remain in the background. Knowledge of English, they realized belatedly, was important. Here many of them—principals and teachers at Japanese language schools—had been busy encouraging and teaching youngsters to learn a second language—Japanese—and they themselves had been satisfied with only one language—Japanese—in an American community. Had they really been a part of their community when they couldn't even communicate satisfactorily with other ethnic groups on an idea level?

Within the huge compound was a low mountain. Climbing this mountain made them forget momentarily that they were prisoners. But when they sat down at the top of the hill, they realized even more forcefully that they were prisoners. Surrounding the compound were the barbed wire fences, watchtowers, armed guards. East, west, north or south, they saw the paraphernalia of imprisonment.

But of what good is freedom unless it is utilized, Ozaki asked. Look at the birds flying overhead. They were free, yet, in a sense, they were not, always following the lead bird to wherever it would take them. Even at home, we thought we were free, but were we, really? Bound by our 8 to 4 jobs and our lead bird employer? Bound to unpleasant monotonous jobs when our hearts yearned to be artists, poets, actors, baseball stars, architects?

Repatriation was another topic discussed over and over again. "Why return to Japan and eat that nation's precious food?" Ozaki asked. "They have so little, even in normal years, because so much of Japan's land is not suitable for farming."

"But why remain here? Wasting precious days and months of my life. I want to be doing something productive...anything. And I want to do it in Japan if I can't be allowed to do it in the U.S."

"Be patient. The war will end soon. Don't go back to Japan now where there's so little food. Let the people in that country have that food. We have a choice. We are given a choice, whether to go back to Japan or to remain in America. The people in Japan have no choice..."

"Remain here and continue being stigmatized as a prisoner when I haven't done anything wrong? You want me to respect a nation that lumps an ethnic group together and charges us with 'possible' disloyalty?"

"Patience," Ozaki repeated, "patience. Soon some of the leaders in this country will realize they made a mistake, putting us in concentration camps and paying for our support, when we could have been contributing to America's war effort without any expense to the government. Meanwhile we are representing 150,000 Japanese back home in Hawai'i. The government couldn't put everyone away, so they selected us. We needn't be servile, even though we have to obey orders. Show these Americans we come in contact with...some of whom never saw a Japanese before...show them what the Japanese are like, and they'll learn to respect us."

"A bishop has to dig trenches and a company president has to scrub toilets? Do we show them we can do such work too?"

"Why not? We can show them there's dignity in work, in any type of work. We're not afraid of getting our hands dirty. Dignity is in the human being, not in the job. Look, many of the guards tell us they're ashamed of having to order us around, as if we're criminals. But, they say, they would be court-martialed unless they follow orders. They say we are being wronged. So already some people understand and respect us."

Then an incident occurred at Fort Sill which shocked them.

Kanesaburo Oshima was a barber from the island of Hawai'i. Although others offered their services free—reading and writing letters in English, mending someone else's coat—Oshima charged for his hair-cuts.

On May 12, 1942, Chikuma and some others were chopping wood for the kitchen stove. Oshima came from another block and asked to borrow a hatchet.

"Each block has its own hatchet, Oshima. Our block has one, your block has one. Why don't you use your block's hatchet?"

"They won't let me have it. And I must have wood for our barrack. It's my responsibility for this week. Please...let me borrow your hatchet for only half an hour."

"We said use your own block's hatchet. Don't you know the kitchen requires a lot of wood? We need this hatchet all the time."

"Please...please..."

"No" The men did not know what Oshima's tentmates knew—that the night before he had been acting strangely while playing *hanafuda*—Japanese cards—with his Kona friends such as Rev. Hozui Nakayama and Rev. Gyokuei Matsuura.

Oshima drooped and walked slowly away. As the men watched, they saw him walking in a circle, as if thinking. Then he began walking faster and faster still in a circle.

"Hey, look at Oshima. Something's wrong. We should have loaned him our hatchet. Somebody, quick, go see what happened to him."

Suddenly Oshima ran to the barbed wire fence and began climbing it, sobbing, "I want to go home...I want to go home..."

A guard close by called, "Stop! Get down or I'll shoot!" Oshima continued climbing. The guard aimed his rifle at Oshima.

"Don't shoot, don't shoot," another guard yelled. "For Pete's sake, don't shoot!"

"Help him, help him," the internees yelled. "Don't shoot. Help him get down!"

It was too late. A shot rang out and Oshima fell.

What the internees hadn't known was that Oshima had twelve

children at home. Even with him working till late at night, it had been a continuous struggle, trying to feed and clothe that many children. Now, with him away, what hardships his wife and children must be undergoing! He constantly worried about his family, but did not confide except in a few: to Rev. Hozui Nakayama, his priest back home and his tentmate at camp; and to Ittetsu Watanabe, who read and wrote his letters for him, for all letters at this time had to be in English!

When the internees pieced together the story, they were sobered and ashamed. They had begrudged a dime for a haircut, but not for a beer. Each internee had been so busy feeling sorry for himself and complaining that he had not had time to consider others and to learn about their concerns and fears. Now they looked at each other with new awareness, as if to ask, "Can I help?"

But it was too late for Oshima.

Rev. Nakayama presided at the funeral services, which all the camp residents attended. They ignored the four machine guns pointed at them; these had been brought in for fear of an uprising.

A few days later, the Spanish Consulate sent someone to investigate the circumstances of the shooting, and the guard who fired the shot was sent to another camp to avoid problems. But beyond that, the internees were not told anything. Oshima was buried in a cemetery in Oklahoma thousands of miles away from home. It would be many years before his eldest son came to take him home to the Kona countryside where the red coffee beans gleamed in the morning sun and the cobalt blue Pacific Ocean sparkled far below. And for Oshima, a barber who never learned why he was selected for internment, the warmth of countryside and men came too late.

CHAPTER 11

LIVINGSTON:

The Panamanians

Uncertainty and insecurity had plagued the Hawai'i internees as they moved from camp to camp. In December, 1941, it had been the Immigration Station in Honolulu. Then had followed Sand Island in January, Angel Island in San Francisco in February, Camp McCoy in Wisconsin in March, Fort Sill in Oklahoma and Camp Forrest in Tennessee in May, and now Livingston, Louisiana in June, 1942. By the time they had learned the rules and regulations of a camp and had accumulated enough scrap lumber to build a shelf, they were told to pack again.

But when they reached Livingston, they sensed permanence. The barracks were not only completed, they were numbered *i-ro-ha-ni*, the

Japanese alphabet. Some other Hawai'i internees were already there, and greeted them with cheers of welcome. But what impressed the newcomers was the kindness of the guards. As they walked from the train station to the camp in the 100-degree weather, staggering not only from the heat but from the heavy duffel bags they were carrying, they were allowed to rest without the threat of being shot. Also, the guards treated them with consideration, and when soldiers from some barracks they were passing tried to take pictures of the stumbling group, the guards yelled out a warning. One soldier who persisted had his camera confiscated. When the internees saw this, they passed the word down the line, "This is going to be a humane camp, a good camp."

Some of the new arrivals staggered into camp bent under the weight of their suitcases. They had been told the suitcases would be brought by truck later, but many would not trust the suitcases out of their sight, since these had once disappeared for three months. They quickly revived when they saw a sign which read "ALOHA." It brought tears to see this word again, this word which symbolized their beloved Hawai'i. How had they lived so many years without consciously appreciating the islands ? Where in the world was there another place like Hawai'i ?

Camp Livingston already had over 700 internees: 400 from the West Coast states, 160 from Panama and Costa Rica, and 166 from Hawai'i. The 180 new arrivals were alphabetically divided into groups and placed in barracks numbered J1 through J4. The West Coast's 400 Japanese were in K1 through K4. The J barracks also included the Central Americans, and Furuya was in J1 which was comprised chiefly of Panamanians.

The soil in the camp was sandy. The barracks were built about three feet above ground in rows that descended a gradual slope. The sand and slope became important to the men, for they found that the best air-conditioner in the 100-degree weather was to dig a hole under a building with the higher portion of the slope serving as a backrest.

When the men sat in their holes, it was like theater seating, all facing forward. At first Furuya was dismayed to see corporation presidents, bishops and school principals crawling under the house and wriggling themselves into comfortable holes, like chickens in the dust. But one day he tried sitting in one and lo and behold! it was indeed several degrees cooler than in the barracks. Quickly he borrowed a scoop and dug his own hole. That, with a newspaper folded into a fan, served as his air-conditioner the rest of the summer.

Although the men could earn $16 a month by working in the kitchen or by chopping firewood, many preferred to "sit it out" because of the heat. And lounging in their holes under the barracks, they reminisced about the past six months.

"Do you remember on the ship coming over to San Francisco and we were locked in the rooms? I had a festering abscess—so full of pus the skin was stretched tight over it—and no one had a pin or needle so I could get the pus out. I pinched the skin, scratched it, and still couldn't get through the skin. Then, one day on my way to lunch, I accidentally banged the abscess against the sharp edge of the bulletin board and the pus spilled out. I didn't have a handkerchief with me and I had to wipe the pus on my shirt. You know, when they took me away from my family and sent me to Sand Island, I was frightened and bitter, but I didn't cry. But the day the pus finally splattered all over me, I cried. The tears just fell and there was nothing I could do about it. But after the pus was out and the tears were gone—I had missed my lunch—I felt like a new man. Now I could accept anything. That tiny irritation had taken the place of my bigger grief, and I felt strong."

"Yes, that was a terrible ten days on the ship, wasn't it? Furuya, do you remember your toothache? I remember you looked like you had the mumps, back at the other camp."

"Do I remember? How can I forget?" Furuya groaned. "My toothache started on Thursday, and Wednesday was the only day we could be taken outside the camp to see a dentist. I suffered for a whole week, and by the following Wednesday, I could hardly tell which tooth was the one with the cavity because they all hurt so much. And that damned dentist wouldn't fill in the tooth. Said it would take too much time, and he was taking us Japs as patients only because the military forced him to. Do you know what he did? He gave me a shot of Novocain but before it took full effect, he yanked my tooth out. That was the first time I realized the helplessness of being a prisoner in a concentration camp. Until then I had thought of myself as a detainee in a government camp. But I wasn't a detainee, I was a prisoner. There was no use fooling myself."

They sat in silence, anger coursing through their bodies. Finally Furuya continued, "Back in Hawai'i, I worked all my life, including Saturdays and Sundays. I would have endless meetings with this organization or that organization. Once my wife told me, 'Do you have to work today? It's Sunday. It's Robert's birthday; we're having a party at lunch.'"

"'Oh, sure,' I'd answered. But once at the store I forgot. Then I went to a meeting. It was dark when I got home. There was such a silence I knew something was wrong. Then I remembered. Robert's birthday. Again."

"'Robert, I'm sorry. I forgot,' I told my son. I gave him $5 but he wouldn't take it."

"'That's OK, papa,' he answered."

"I would feel terrible. But the following year it would be the same. Before I knew it he had grown up and began spending birthdays with his friends. He didn't need me anymore. I had not been a part of his childhood."

"I know...I know. I too used to work every day. I used to wish for one week's vacation, even one day off. But I thought my store couldn't run without me, so I would be there first thing in the morning and was the last to leave at night. And now look, almost one year away from the store and my wife writes that it is business as usual...in fact, business is better. Now I realize I wasn't indispensable. I've learned my lesson. When I go back, I'm going to give more time to my family. What's money? So I can donate to this organization or that organization and be thought of as a big shot? What a fool I was. I never thought of weighing priorities in considering my time and actions. I just did things by habit." They lapsed into an uncomfortable silence.

"Poor Mrs. Harada..." Furuya murmured suddenly. "Imagine, in one week, losing her husband in a tragic death, having her daughter taken from her, losing her job. If only that pilot had crashed into the ocean instead. And look what it did to Mr. Shintani, too. He never talks to us, here at camp. We maybe had reason to be interned, since we did business with Japan firms and we entertained Japanese naval ships. But Shintani was guiltless. He had no crime but his Japanese face, Japanese name and citizenship. He even had a Hawaiian wife and half-Hawaiian children ...Have any of us made an extra-special effort to be friends with him? Have we encouraged him to join in our activities?"

Everyone looked at everyone else. Then they all strained the sand at their side, as if to strain the guilt from their conscience.

In August, 19 of them were told they were to return to Hawai'i. Dr. Kazuo Miyamoto, who had been a leader and tireless physician, was one of the first to be called. What were they to do without him, the always calm and capable doctor who came even in the middle of the night if they asked for him? Also slated to return were Rev. Kenjitsu Tsuha, Rev. Shigeo Fujino, Noriaki Atsuumi from the wholesaler Shimaya Shoten, Shinsaburo Sumida of Honolulu Sake Brewery, and others. Why had they been selected?

Soon the reason was made clear. They were all American citizens, although most were *kibei*, or citizens educated in Japan. Nineteen men returned to Hawai'i in July, but instead of being freed, they were rearrested and thrown back into the Sand Island camp.

At Camp Livingston, the rest of the internees planned and organized different activities to keep themselves alert and physically well.

A Rev. Kano from Grand Island, Nebraska, started a botany-farming class. He had few enrollees at first, as no one wanted to be out in the heat. But when he started taking students outside the barbed wire fences and into cool gullies, he gained an overflow class that had to be divided into two sections.

In the gullies, the men encountered eels almost two feet long which slithered in the wet rocks and slimy grass. These reminded the Hawai'i men of snakes; the internees were as afraid of eels as they were of snakes. They also saw armadillos for the first time, and spiders identified as poisonous.

They found other objects in the pine groves. One was a six-inch oval rock, often lying on the paths they used. When they kicked it aside, they found it had several pairs of legs. This was the land turtle, whose tiny babies could fit on one's thumbnail.

Another pine grove object was the snake. There were several varieties. The Peruvians taught the Hawai'i men which were poisonous and which were not, but the Hawaiians could never learn. They feared all snakes—every color, every size, moving or still, dead or alive. But the Peruvians merely stamped on the snake's head, even poisonous ones, slit the snake lengthwise, and pulled the skin off in one swift movement. They used the skin to make belts or purses, and ate the snakes broiled.

Furuya, on one of his field trips, found a stone hollowed out with another stone in it. It sounded like a rattle, and brought back memories of when his son, Robert, was a baby. At night, Furuya would rattle the stone before going to sleep, and when he forgot, someone would murmur, "Furuya forgot his rattle."

As the days grew cooler, the men began preparing to play softball. Furuya was responsible for collecting the equipment and for serving as umpire.

Being an umpire was not an easy job, he found, as pitchers would challenge his every call. "You're a junk umpire," one pitcher would yell.

"That's because you're a junk pitcher," he would yell back. In the years that followed, even in Hawai'i, the two greeted each other, "Hello, junk umpire! Oh, hello, junk pitcher!"

But being the equipment manager had its rewards. He was allowed to go outside the barbed wire fence to the Army clubhouse to gather the equipment. One day he brought back a stool and some plants. But what made the others envious was that he had had a highball.

"What did it taste like? Was it cold, with ice in it? What does the inside of the clubhouse look like?"

Furuya remembered the coolness of the spacious room, with greenery against the walls, the clink of frosted glasses as the service men sat at the tables, munching peanuts and chips. There had been a real air-conditioner, short-skirted waitresses, and laughter that sounded natural. The highball had slid down his throat with a smooth deliciousness that had warmed and cooled him at the same time.

He saw the eagerness in the internees' faces, their lack of jealousy, their friendliness. "Nah, wasn't anything special. Just a drink. And the clubhouse ain't so hot. Let's play ball!"

With cool weather, the men also held classes. Some men offered English, Japanese and Spanish classes. Others taught classes in woodcarving, painting, calligraphy, business, geography, history, philosophy and *shakuhachi*, Japan's unique flute-like instrument. Each man shared his talent.

They also played golf. The J section made a 9-hole golf course. The K section, the West Coast Japanese section, made another 9-hole course. Together they could play an 18-hole game. Some of the men had never held a golf club before. They had been too busy working. But as the days passed, they began to improve so much they complained the course was too plain. They wanted a sand trap here, a water hazard there, as in a real golf course.

Some of the other men decided to put on a play. Producing a play was easier said than done. First the group had to beg, borrow or steal pots, pans and other objects that could produce sound—this would be their band. Itsuo Hamada, from Maui, wrote a play. Costumes had to be devised, and many a window curtain and pillowcase were sacrificed. Music was written and rehearsed. Makeup was improvised, including wigs for women's roles from dyed potato sack fibers. The Panamanians went into the mountains to cut wood for the benches. This required cutting down a tree, splicing the trunk to make benchsize slats, sanding the wood to eliminate splinters, and cutting and sanding other pieces of wood to make "horses" for the slats.

The play was a big success financially, for each person donated a dime to see the play. More important, there was a special feeling of closeness among the camp members involved in the play. A decision was made that night: let's have another play within four months.

In this feeling of camaraderie, there was a sudden chill. The Panamanians could be seen whispering among themselves, but would stop when a Hawai'i internee walked by. Finally one of the Central Americans approached Furuya, since he lived in their barrack.

"Mr. Furuya, you know the benches we made for the play?"

"Sure. It's in the dining room."

"That's the problem. It's not. Some of the Hawai'i men have taken the benches and are using them for shelves and bookcases. We think it's unfair of them to use the benches as private property."

"I'm sorry. I didn't know that."

"Well, maybe the first person thought taking one bench would be OK. But someone else took another one, and so on, and now, when we put on the next play, we'll have a hard time getting the benches back because the people would be accustomed to them. They would consider it their private property by that time."

"Let me see what I can do," Furuya promised.

It was only a few weeks later that Mr. Ogata from Hawai'i needed an operation for ulcers. But the hospital had no blood plasma. Would any of the over 300 men from Hawai'i be willing to be tested and donate blood if necessary?

Most of the Hawai'i men were elderly so they were fearful. The food was not too nutritious, they said, and they were not healthy. Could Furuya ask the Panamanians instead?

Furuya hesitated. It was only a few weeks since they had been resentful about the "borrowed" benches. How would they feel about the Hawai'i men now asking them for a favor? But it was Mr. Ogata's life that was at stake, so Furuya approached the leader of the Panamanians to ask if his men would be willing to help Mr. Ogata by going for a blood test and then donating blood if it was needed. "Sure." Six of them volunteered unhesitatingly and immediately. Furuya wept. He was so proud of being with the Panamanians.

But Furuya could not help but be struck by the difference culture and environment had made among the same Japanese spread among different cultures of Hawai'i, the Mainland states, Panama and the South American countries. One day, Commandant Dan Weaver, an extremely neat person, suggested they dry their bedding since it was such a nice sunny day, and winter would soon be here.

Each man in J1, which included the Panamanians and Furuya, carried out his cot, blankets, and pillow. They hung the blankets on a fence, to let the breeze flow through and freshen them. They plumped the pillows and left them on the cots, which were in any direction they had been placed in.

The Panamanians looked over to see what J2 was doing. The men there had placed the cots in a neat row. Each pillow was at the head of each cot. The blankets had been folded neatly into an oblong of about 24" by 36" and placed at the foot of the bed. The Panamanians frantically sought Furuya.

"Look...look at J2. They're so neat. We aren't neat. Weaver might not like our section. We look like messy housewives. Let's do as J2 did," they implored.

"But the Colonel said to air the blankets. If they're folded that way, the blankets can't be aired. Look at our blankets. See the breeze blowing through them. How fresh they will be when we sleep under them tonight," Furuya answered. "And what does it matter where the pillow is? We put our pillows where we think they'll get the greatest amount of sun and air. So don't worry."

"But Colonel Weaver likes things neat. He doesn't think the way you do. He doesn't go by logic. He goes by looks."

"Nonsense. Colonel Weaver is not that type of man..." But Furuya saw the desperation in their eyes, their fear of again being the focus of undesirable attention. So he said, "OK, if you think it's better. Do it the way J2 did."

Later he discussed this fear with the Hawai'i men.

"What kind of environment did they live in, to be so fearful of being different? We in Hawai'i, we've always been free to do things and live the way we wanted."

What the Panamanians later told the Hawai'i internees was that those who lived in the Panama "Canal Zone" had been arrested on Dec. 7 and could take with them only the clothes they had on. They were held for 24 hours by the police without food and water.

The next day, they were turned over to American authorities and transported to Mainland U.S. camps. Their money was confiscated and their homes looted. The Japanese government had formally sent a note of protest on October 1, 1942, through the Spanish Embassy, for the treatment the Panamanian Japanese had received. The Japanese government also knew the American authorities were collecting Japanese nationals from other governments, such as Bolivia and Peru and even from European countries to exchange with American prisoners held in Japan prisons.[1]

The desire of the Panamanians to be accepted was not fully understood by the Hawai'i internees until much later. By that time it was too late to tell them, "*Ganbatte!* You are men, you are *yuushi*—heroes! You have been knocked down but you have always gotten up off your knees. Yes, you did *ganbaru*, and we are proud of you"

One day, some West Coasters who had arrived from Missoula, Montana, had a sale of petrified rock. These were of different colors, and cost from $3 to $5. Furuya longed for one, a purple-blue stone that changed color depending on the light. But $5 for an unpolished rock when $3.50 was what he used monthly for toothpaste, razor blades, Band-Aid and other necessities? He steeled himself against such extravagance and returned to his barrack. But all afternoon the beauty of the stone haunted him. Finally he said, "I'm buying it for my wife and daughter. The colors of our sky here, our mountains in the distance, our twilights are in that stone. I want to share those colors, my feelings about our skies and twilights...with them."

Thus rationalizing he went back, only to find that the collection had been sold. There was nothing left to do but go back to his hollowed-out rattle, and shake it until the unfulfilled desire for the purple-blue stone was driven out of him.

CHAPTER 12

KAZUO SAKAMAKI:

War Prisoner #1

Kazuo Sakamaki, U.S.'s Pacific War Prisoner #1, was first sighted washed ashore at one of Oahu's beaches, barely breathing.

When the internees saw him, he was at Sand Island, housed in a separate hut which was in a 10'x10' "birdcage" and in full view of everyone since it was near the entrance to the camp. His only contact was with Sgt. Lance Moran, who took his food to him. Internees were forbidden to talk to him, or he to anyone, internee or guard.

One day the internees saw his face disfigured with burns. The men were furious. "That's against international law," they whispered, "to torture him like that just to get information. Let's talk to Captain Eifler."

U.S. Pacific War Prisoner Kazuo Sakamaki, captured Dec. 7, 1941 on one of Hawai'i's beaches, was isolated in the "birdcage" behind double lines of barbed wire fences.

Photo Courtesy U.S. Army (Ret.) Col. Carl F. Eifler

But Sgt. Moran, who was trusted by the men, explained that Sakamaki himself had disfigured his face with his one cigarette allowed per day. He had been informed he was to have a picture taken, and had acknowledged his disgrace of capture with a symbolic design—an inverted triangle—on his face.

It was at Camp McCoy that the Hawai'i internees were able to talk with him. The first night at Camp McCoy, there was some commotion at the door. MPs entered with Sakamaki and explained they did not have a place for him. It was March and freezing cold in Wisconsin. Could Sakamaki stay with the Hawai'i contingent? And could the men explain the situation to Sakamaki?

"Of course," Dr. Kazuo Miyamoto nodded. "Sakamaki-san, this is not Sand Island. At that camp you were forbidden to talk with us. But here at this camp, the commander is asking that you stay with us until a barrack can be prepared for you. You know how cold it is here. You cannot sleep in an unheated barrack."

Sakamaki bowed and said, "*Onegai shimasu.* Thank you."

That night, because of the opportunity provided them, they all plied him with questions. How did he get on O'ahu? Was he the only one captured? What could he tell them about the war?

"Please don't ask me any questions," he pleaded. "As a Japan military officer, I am unable to answer, either to you or to the Americans who have been quizzing me practically every day."

The next day he was transferred to another barrack, now with a 24-hour guard. The men noticed his eyes were dilated and he walked as if in a trance. Later, Sakamaki was to write in his memoirs that he could not remember what happened to him at Sand Island or at Camp McCoy. He had effectively blocked out the indignity of being put in a "birdcage" and of being guarded night and day, without any privacy.

Sakamaki's story began months before Pearl Harbor. Exuberantly, he had written to his parents to say he was going to bring honor to them. How, he was not allowed to elaborate. But in his farewell letter,

ENSIGN KAZUO SAKAMAKI: U.S.'s Pacific War Prisoner #1, Sakamaki was the skipper of a midget submarine which malfunctioned and washed ashore on Oʻahu. Photo Courtesy Honolulu Advertiser Below: TWO-MAN MIDGET SUBMARINE: A military secret in Japan, the midget sub carried only two torpedoes. Its crew was not expected to return.
Photo Courtesy Hawaiʻi War Records Depository, UH-Mānoa

129

he saw his gift of self to motherland, and through it, to his parents. He was young, but it could not be helped. He would be like the camellia which drops whole at the height of its beauty, not wilting, not falling petal by petal, or drying brown and brittle on the stem.

Kazuo Sakamaki, at the time of the letter, was an ensign in the Japanese Navy, but now he was to be a skipper. Of course the ship was only a 6-1/2-foot by 78-foot two-man midget submarine, and it carried only two torpedoes. Nevertheless, he was its skipper. To expect to return alive after firing the torpedoes was considered difficult if not impossible, but what greater glory was there than to die for one's country and for one's emperor? Sadly, neither country nor emperor knew that such subs existed. Only five of the midget subs were being tested.

Although the tiny sub was in perfect condition in home waters, Sakamaki found on the evening of Dec. 6 (Dec. 7 by his watch) the gyrocompass did not work and he would not be able to steer accurately. To determine direction, he had to raise the sub and peek through the periscope, a dangerous move, for he could be spotted by the enemy. And spotted he was. Depth bombs shook him and his partner, Petty Officer Kiyoshi Inagaki. The craft tumbled like a toy boat in a bathtub when the water is turned on full force. The sub filled with fumes and smoke; the batteries leaked. Even the periscope was lost. Eventually the craft grounded on a bed of coral.

Instead of having his sub fall into enemy hands, Sakamaki decided to blow it up and destroy it. He lighted the fuse to a bomb prepared for that purpose and he and Inagaki scrambled out the hatch, expecting to be blown any moment into bits. They jumped into the cold water and swam hastily away from the sub, but there was no explosion. He called out to Inagaki; he heard an agonized cry. Sakamaki lost consciousness, knowing that everything that could go wrong... absolutely everything...had gone wrong.

When next he opened his eyes, he saw an American soldier with a gun looking curiously at the half-drowned Japanese dressed ludicrous-

KAZUO SAKAMAKI

ly in a leather jacket and a loincloth. Inagaki was found later, drowned. Only the midget sub that was to have been a military secret survived. The dreams of both the sub's designer and of Sakamaki died.

Thus it was that a fresh-faced, patriotic youth, born during the last year of World War I, on November 18, 1919 on the small island of Shikoku, Japan, was to become the U.S.'s first Pacific prisoner on the first day of World War II for the Americans. He was to learn about this country from the Hawai'i Japanese with whom he lived for many months.

At Camp Forrest in Tennessee, Sakamaki looked happier. A Mr. King from the International YMCA paid a visit to the prisoners, and he must have said something to Major Laemmle, for after his visit, Sakamaki was allowed greater freedom. He could now talk to others and attend classes and the movies. But day and night he was still escorted by a guard with a club.

The same Dr. King also spoke to the Hawai'i internees. "My work consists chiefly in supplying educational and recreational material to prisoners from both sides of the war," he explained. "There are hundreds and thousands of men behind barbed wire. Don't sit here pitying yourselves. Profit from your days here. Look at Albert Schweitzer. He was a World War I prisoner. When he was in captivity he had free time for the first time, and he composed three musicals and wrote two books. Among you there must be many who are also creative. Use your time wisely."

After King's visit, Sakamaki relaxed. He was especially friendly with Rev. Ninryo Nago, who had fought in the Japanese cavalry in the Russo-Japanese war, was wounded, and taken captive in Manchuria.

"To be a captive is not a disgrace," Nago told Sakamaki. "Alive, we can serve our country again. Dying for our country may be the supreme sacrifice, but it is not for the greatest good. We can serve our country in various ways." The two became good friends, and when, in

June, 1942, some 36 Japan prisoners were brought in from Midway and another 50 from Wake Island, Sakamaki spoke to them the way Nago had talked to him.

"Being alive gives us an opportunity to serve our country once again," he told the new prisoners. But the POWs needed time to absorb this philosophy. Their captain, Captain Nakamune, cut a three-inch slash on his throat, but he survived. "I did not carry out my responsibility well enough," he moaned. "That's why we lost."

"What? Do you mean the fate of the battle at Midway depended on one ship, one man? Was the responsibility of the outcome all yours? Would you have taken all the acclaim in case Japan had won?"

"No..."

"Of course not. Battles are cooperative efforts. You fought the best you could, and the Americans fought the best they could. That's all we in the military can do...do our best with what we have." He paused...how could he not remember his faulty mini-sub?

Sakamaki did not know then that Japan's secret code had been broken, and Admiral Halsey knew in advance the itinerary of Admiral Yamamoto to Rabaul and Bougainville in the South Pacific. Long-range air force P38s from Guadalcanal intercepted Admiral Yamamoto's plane in mid-flight, shooting it down and killing the admiral.

In fact, few knew that Japan's codes were broken way before Pearl Harbor, and messages were decoded, exposing Japan's plans to a few, including the president but not Hawai'i's Army and Navy commanders.

One day Sakamaki walked into a pine grove with Furuya. "You Americans are so lucky..." Sakamaki began.

"Americans? We're not Americans. We often think we are, but during emergencies such as this, look what happened to us. We realize we're Japanese..."

"Ah, you have a Japanese face and name, and you use the Japanese language, but inside you're no longer Japanese. You have a different philosophy. For example, we in Japan don't feel much responsibility for others, although we're taught to fight and die for our country. But then country—the term country—is an ideal, a nebulous idea. We're trained from an early age to believe that our country comes first—before ourselves, before our families. We must be able to sacrifice ourselves and our families for our country. But that way we're not relating to individual people, to our friends, our neighbors...people who have names and faces and sorrows and joyful experiences and worries. The country comes first, and within it are these people...But another way of looking at it is, these people are precious, these people are worth fighting for...and these people constitute our country. It's like looking from two ends of the same kaleidoscope.

"I think that's what makes this country, America, great. You care for each other. I see you sharing your sad moments, your happy moments. You almost live each other's lives..."

"Well," Furuya said, "There's so few of us, and nothing else to do. We have to listen to others and even to our own conscience. We now have the time and opportunity to evaluate our past and our values, our expectations, our goals in life, our relationships with others."

"You have the Japanese in you, but you also have the American..."

"Perhaps it's the Hawaiian influence, more than the American influence," Furuya mused. "In Hawai'i there's something that's called *ohana* or extended family. That's a large family relationship where members care and share with each other. The fish they catch, the taro they raise, the weaving of the *lauhala* for floor mats, the wood for fire, the fruits and vegetables they raise cooperatively, all these they share...maybe not equally, but according to the amount of work put in. It's similar to our *kenjinkai*, except that it's a more tight-knit group."

"*Ohana*? In Japanese it means a flower! That relationship—of caring and sharing—is as beautiful as a flower."

"And do you know that in old Hawai'i, and even today to some extent, the Hawaiians have what is called a 'calabash' cousin? I used to hear Hawaiians say, 'So and so is my calabash cousin,' and I would ask, 'On your father's side or your mother's side?' and they would answer, 'Neither! He's a calabash cousin…'"

"What's a calabash cousin?"

"A calabash is a big round gourd cut in half, dried, and used as a container. Well, when there's a birth, marriage, emergency such as fire or flood, or death in a family, people gather to help. Whoever comes drops an offering into the calabash, without a name identifying who gave how much. Can you imagine? There's no way the receiver can know how much the giver gave. You see, the giver gives from his heart, and according to what he can share or wants to give to the new couple or the bereaved family. That is a true friend or a calabash cousin!"

"Then there's no way to know who gave $1 or who gave $50?"

"Yes. And it doesn't matter to the giver because he's giving, not to be acknowledged for his gift, but because he wants to share in that happy or sad occasion. In Japan…and in Hawai'i…we put our money in envelopes with our name and address on the outside."

"Calabash cousin!" Sakamaki said softly. Then he added, "Furuya-san, may I be your calabash cousin?"

Furuya began assessing the Hawai'i internees with greater awareness. Did they really care and share the way Sakamaki said? He thought of Masayuki Chikuma, who was always joking, chanting legends and reciting folklore to while away the time. He was so positive in his actions and conversations. Yet he was mischievous enough to make sake from rice, wine from raisins and over-ripe fruit, and thoughtful enough to share these odd-tasting concoctions with different groups in the barracks.

Then there was Otojiro Ozaki, the teacher from Hilo. Ozaki was the philosopher-poet, taking a specific incident and relating it to the whole of life. Ozaki was that rare individual who could detach Ozaki the poet from Ozaki the man and view life from a different plane, like a circling eagle observing the vast 180-degree world below and around him, and at the same time noticing a tiny mouse scurrying in the open fields. He could see the vast forest, but he would also be aware of the fuzz on the under-side of a new tree leaf.

There was Katsukichi Kida, the nephew of Sutematsu Kida, the sampan skipper killed on the morning of December 8, 1941 as he was returning from a fishing trip. During the winter, Katsukichi would make many trips from the dining hall to the barracks to bring food for the aged and the ill, so they could remain in their warm beds. He would clean around their buildings, and even sweep the snow off the roof, although he had once slid from roof to ground with a broom still in his hand. When others asked, "Kida-san..." he never had a prior commitment, a sore back, a cold, or a headache. "Hai!" he would promise and he always kept his promise.

Sakamaki was right, Furuya acknowledged. It took an outsider to see the good in these Hawai'i men who were worried about themselves and their families, who complained and grumbled occasionally, but who cared for those about them.

Things were progressing well when Koichi Iida received a telegram stating that Mrs. Iida was critically ill. Could he receive permission to return to Hawai'i to visit his wife?

To his surprise, the commandant said he could. A guard would have to accompany him, and Iida would have to pay for the guard's air fare. This was of little concern to Iida, if only he could see his wife of so many years just one more time.

But getting seats on the Clipper was another matter. Frantically Iida went to the office to inquire four or five times a day. Had the officials received any word?

While Iida was still reporting to the office, his bags packed, another telegram came saying Mrs. Iida had died. So this was what might happen to them! Many of the internees were in their late sixties, and they and their wives had labored long hours after their emigration to Hawai'i. They remembered the terrifying bubonic plague and the disastrous fire of 1900 which had wiped out several city blocks and their homes and belongings. They remembered the sugar strike of 1922 when they and many others were driven from their plantation homes for participating in the strike. They remembered the Great Depression of 1929 which had wiped out their precious savings. After all that sacrifice in search of a new life and a new home where they could live comfortably, was this to be their method of separation? Not to comfort one another at the death bed ? Not to give the last drop of water and to whisper her name one last time? The Japanese never showed their love openly, but a touch of her face, that clasp of her hand, and she would have understood that love had always been there.

Then it was Gosaku Masuda who died. Actually, the first of the internees to die in camp had been Hisahiko Kokubo on March 9, 1942 at Sand Island. Kanesaburo Oshima had been shot at Fort Sill on May 12, 1942, and Itsuo Inazaki had died on June 18. He was followed by Yoichi Kagimoto on July 27, 1942. The numbers were few, but their deaths had been so senseless; had they been in their home communities they would have been alive!

Rev. Gigyo Ozawa officiated at Masuda's funeral, assisted by 58 priests, 22 Shinto priests, and seven Christian minsters from Hawai'i and the Mainland. As the priests chanted the *hakkotsu no gobunsho*, the voices rang in the dining hall and the resonant chant wafted into the pine groves outside. Next came the song *Mihotoke ni idakarete*...wrapped in Buddha's arms you go westward. Your living being goes, and we feel so sad and lonely...as you go wrapped in Buddha's arms..."

There were only a few flowers. It was freezing cold in mid-

December. Poor Masuda, Furuya mourned. He had always liked Hawai'i's warm weather, and now he was to remain in cold and desolate Louisiana among strangers he had never met.

The internees found they were to move again. 280 of them were to be sent to Missoula, Montana. Furuya was one of them, and he remembered the purple-blue stone he had coveted that had come from that camp.

Others chose to go to Kooskia, Idaho, where they would be paid well...as much as $40 a month, they were told...to work on road construction. One, a Mr. Bamba, was sent his lonely way to Camp Kennedy in Texas with the Peruvians. Some men were slated for Jerome, Arkansas, to be reunited with their families. Kazuo Sakamaki and the Japan POWs were to return to Camp McCoy in Wisconsin. The rest were to be sent to Santa Fe, New Mexico.

There was a soft spring rain, the day before they were to move. The Georgia pines sparkled tiny white flowers, and the raindrops on bushes shone bravely in the early morning sun. Why did they have to leave now, when the tomatoes were doing so well?

That last night, at Livingston, Louisiana, they wrote farewell poems:

Pine shoots grow taller and taller.
They say the war will end soon,
But we watch the pine shoots grow.

Today we are allowed
To pick up rocks to polish.
Let us pick up rocks.

In a hut wrapped in snow,
We sing our hymns.

Although we leave tomorrow,
Tonight we water the plants.[2]

It was the last time they were to see Kazuo Sakamaki, Pacific War Prisoner #1. Saying goodbye to him was like saying goodbye to a fellow Hawai'i internee or to a brother. No, it was even more than that. It was like saying goodbye to a part of one's self.

"Goodbye, calabash cousin," Sakamaki whispered.

"Goodbye, calabash cousin," Furuya answered.

"*Ganbatte, neh?*" Be strong...don't give up...

"Hai, *ganbaru yo!*" Yes, I'll hang on...

CHAPTER 13

LORDSBURG:

Flower in the Crannied Wall

While the Livingston, Louisiana, camp internees slowly adjusted to living behind barbed wire, a different group of Hawai'i internees was seething in Lordsburg, New Mexico. This camp was shared by about 250 men from Hawai'i who had gone in five shiploads in June, August, September and October, 1942. There was also a large number of West Coast internees.

The five groups reached Lordsburg's train station at different times of the day. Matsujiro Otani arrived at 9 p.m.; it was midnight when he reached the camp. George Hoshida reached the camp at 2:30 p.m. It was 110 degrees in the afternoon, but the men were lined up, four abreast for roll call. Then they walked in the sizzling desert heat, and when they reached camp, they were again subjected to roll call. As soon as that was completed, cooks and kitchen helpers were hurried into the unfamiliar kitchen to prepare that night's dinner. There was only one faucet of water. The buildings, designed for 1,500, were not yet completed.

Yasutaro Soga was more fortunate. Because he arrived later in the year, he, Yoshio Koike and 48 others were greeted with a party.

Lordsburg, "the village of God," was in New Mexico, about 25 miles from Arizona and 100 miles from Texas. Although over 4,000 feet above sea level, it was hot in September. In winter, the weather plunged to several degrees below zero. The limestone ground was not conducive to growing things, and the sandstorms were fierce. The internees knew they were there for the duration of the war, but to the Indians in the surrounding area, this inhospitable land was home.

At Lordsburg, the internees again had a form of self-rule. Each 1000 men were divided into four groups of 250 each, with each subgroup led by a "mayor." This self-rule allowed them the opportunity to discuss incidents more openly.

One of the first incidents that arose at Lordsburg had to do with two West Coasters who were being brought in from Bismarck, North Dakota, on July 27, 1942. Toshiro Obata and Hirota Isomura who had arrived with 147 others were too ill to walk to the camp with the rest. A guard, thinking the two waiting for a car at the station were escapees, shot and killed them.

Isomura, 57, had owned a sampan used for fishing; this must have been the reason for his internment. Obata had been dedicated to his Buddhist church, and he had been active in school activities.

When news of the shooting reached the camp, there was anger and bitterness as well as a gnawing grief even among the Hawai'i men that the two had to die under those circumstances. Dr. Teichi Furukawa and a Dr. Akimoto requested an autopsy to determine whether the bullets had entered from the back to the front—which might indicate they were trying to run away. The internees couldn't imagine how someone with 103-degree fever could run far or fast. Or had the bullets entered from the front, as they sat helplessly, perhaps with eyes closed? The request for the autopsy was refused.

The shooting was on July 27. It was not till October 2 that the Army began investigating the case.

The guard who had shot them was from Boston, 28, and married. He had not been an excitable, immature, just-drafted 18-year-old. He testified they were trying to escape. The court would not reveal to the internees the result of the investigation.

Another unpleasant occurrence had to do with having to work at heavy labor outside the camp. Genji Mihara from El Paso, Texas, told the Lordsburg officials that according to Geneva Convention rules, internees were not to be used for heavy labor. The Hawai'i men acquiesced. The men quit reporting for work.

The officials did not force them to return but they terminated the newspaper, denied the use of radio and canteen privileges, turned lights off early, and cancelled recreational activities. The disturbed men sent telegrams to the Spanish Consul. Finally the Spanish ambassador from New Orleans came with a state department official to explore the issue.

The camp commander reported that outside labor was voluntary. Not so, Company 10 representatives said. "Who would work voluntarily in 110-degree heat? Besides, pick and shovel work for elderly, undernourished priests not used to such work is inhumane."

"Men in the other compounds work too. They don't complain," the camp commander insisted.

"Yes, but Compound 3 has 1,000 men, and our company, Company 10, has only 191. The number of men requisitioned is the same, so our men must report more frequently. Not only that, Compound 3 seems to have chiefly indoor work, and only during the morning hours, when it is cooler..."

"It just looks that way to you..."

"Why not check the records, to compare with the records we have? To see who was assigned where and when during the past month?"

For complaining to outside agencies, the men in Company 10 had more privileges taken away.

It was in this type of antagonistic atmosphere that a third incident occurred.

The camp was building a road outside the barbed wire fence above the hospital area. About 30 men followed a tractor, and as it softened the limestone, the men shoveled the dirt away from the road.

Early one morning, the tractor broke down. The driver said he would have to go to town to get parts, and advised the men to return to their compounds and report again after lunch. This was before 10 a.m., earlier than their usual time for a break.

The watchful guard in one of the towers must have seen the men returning to the compound early. He reported to the office that there was a strike in progress, but no one came to investigate.

That afternoon, the internees followed the tractor which had been repaired. Suddenly a captain from the MP Detachment came riding up on a bicycle. Angrily he sought out the work leader. Accusing the men of going on strike, he pulled out his revolver and fired a shot close to the work leader's feet. The man was astounded. He did not know of the telephone call by the guard to the office, or that they were under suspicion of calling a strike. The captain continued to berate them and threatened as to the consequences if they did not work properly. "But we have been working properly," the work leader answered.

"Then why didn't you work this morning?" the Captain wanted to know.

"Because the tractor broke down. The driver had to go to town to get parts and he said to report back after lunch, which is what we did. What did we do wrong?"

The captain looked a little sheepish, cursed the guards, and drove off.

The work leader picked up the bullet and cap for evidence, and the men continued working until it was time to return to the compound. That night the "mayors" of the different sub-groups decided to request an investigation of the incident. There had been no fault on the part of the internees. The driver of the tractor and the guards would substantiate their story.

When they met with Major Whitmarsh, the provost marshal, he agreed that it had been unfortunate. But each man had been trying to do his duty. The guard wanted to nip any strike in the bud. The captain wanted to discourage rebellion.

"But don't you people investigate before shooting?" the internees asked.

The captain was transferred elsewhere, but no one found it necessary to say, "I'm sorry." The men's respect for the Americans plunged to a new low.

Just as the Hawai'i internees at Livingston found differences in fellow Japanese from Panama and Costa Rica, so the Hawai'i internees at Lordsburg found differences between "stateside" internees and Hawai'i internees. Even their perspective on internment differed.

The Hawai'i internees thought of themselves as "detainees." Being "detained" was not as threatening or traumatic as being "interned" or "incarcerated."

"Bull! Don't be naive," the statesiders chided the islanders. "This is an internment camp. We're internees..."

"Well, it depends upon how we interpret these words..."

"No matter how you interpret it, you're in an internment camp, a concentration camp. Barbed wire fences. Armed guards. Vicious dogs. Bayonets. Practically free labor."

"But we've been treated well."

"You have? So long as you're treated well, you don't care about the others who had their homes taken, their jobs lost, their education interrupted? What about those who are at Leupp, Arizona? What about one of your own men, Rev. K. Tsuha? He and about 69 others, some of them teenagers, are isolated on a Navaho Indian Reservation. They know we've been wronged. You don't think you've been wronged? How many years have you lived in Hawai'i? 30 years? 40 years? And it's OK if you're taken away from your home on five minutes notice?" And not charged with a specific crime?"

"That's true. But we've been treated OK. Look, we have to be intelligent and accept certain actions," the Hawai'i men insisted. "During the first few days, conditions in Hawai'i were chaotic. No one knew whether the Japanese troops would land on O'ahu. To the young mainland soldiers, we look just like Japanese from Japan, so we had to be on guard. The young MPs were trigger happy. They went around with their guns cocked, for the next life to go could be their own. In a situation such as that, they wanted instant obedience, and we gave it to them. We didn't talk about Constitutional rights or democratic ideals. We weren't passive; we actually interpreted why the officials acted that way. We knew the ones with the guns were just as frightened as the ones without.

"Then, as time passed and higher-level officers and even a general or two inspected our camp—back at Sand Island—orders came through that we were to be treated humanely. Camp officials in general reverted to being fellow human beings again. So you see we had to gauge time and place.

"We haven't been dissenters or protesters like you Mainlanders. Many of you are young; most of us are older immigrants. You see, we came by choice to work in another land, a foreign land. We were able to withstand temporary hardships for a future goal. We were day-to-day workers on plantations for a time, but we were also thinkers, planners. We could submerge our immediate goals for a larger future goal. Of course there are exceptions. Some of us immigrants turned out loafers but there are exceptions in almost everything. In general, however, we Japanese in Hawai'i planned for the future, and we endured

144

temporary hardships because the future goal was in sight...not in everybody's eyes, but in our own. This internment, too, is a temporary hardship..."

"I see. Thanks for letting us know why you do what you do," the Statesiders said. "As for me, I still wonder if evacuation was the only choice open to us. If we had refused to move, would they have imprisoned 110,000 of us—babies, the ill, the elderly—in their prisons? Would the Army have dared ship 110,000 Japanese to Japan? What would the world have said to that?"

The questions were moot. Who cared what the Japanese internees thought ? Only the Japanese internees cared...

Many Hawai'i internees, including Yasutaro Soga and Yoshio Koike, would walk each evening along the barbed wire fences to discuss concerns they would not have discussed during their hectic days and nights in Hawai'i. Or they would sit on some hill to watch the sunset or the early stars that shone so brilliantly in that starkly lonesome, pristine desert. They had time to talk to others, to themselves, and to "think things through."

There was an oversupply of Shinto and Buddhist priests and even Christian ministers. They grew spiritually, but in the end, it was Nature that was the greatest spiritual teacher. The internees saw beauty and meaning in sand that shifted everlastingly and made beautiful patterns at the whim of the wind. Now, finally, they understood the symbolism of the famous Ryoanji Gardens in Kyoto. They saw new beauty in the way rocks had been shaped through the centuries by sand, wind and rain. They saw beauty in the desert that stretched endlessly to the horizon, and they saw beauty in the stars and a moon so large and clear it seemed one could tear a hole in its center should one extend a finger too high.

And, at their feet, they found more beauty and symbolism in the tiny desert flowers which bloomed for a day, flowers as delicate and exquisite as any hothouse flower.

Soga, a poet at heart, was reminded of a poem by Thomas Gray, an English writer. Was it "Elegy Written in a Country Churchyard"? he asked himself.

"I remember memorizing that poem half a century ago. Funny that I should remember that, when I can't remember what I ate for lunch yesterday. The poem went, 'Full many a flower is born to blush unseen And waste its sweetness on the desert air.' But is it necessary for every flower to be seen by man? And if not seen, is it wasted? Doesn't every flower, every act, exist for itself, and not for others"

"There you go again, talking philosophy," a Statesider said.

But Soga continued, "Listen, what does a Westerner do? Lord Tennyson, an Englishman, wrote:

> Flower in the crannied wall,
> I pluck you out of the crannies,
> I hold you here, root and all, in my hand.
> Little flower—but if I could understand
>
> What you are, root and all, and all in all,
> I could know what God and man is.

A Japanese...an Asian...wouldn't pull out the flower. No, the flower has its place on this earth, and Man has his place. Why destruct what is in Nature to understand Self? No, the Japanese would appreciate even that which is being discarded, as in this poem:

> The garden is now
> Left unswept for maple leaves
> Flutter from their boughs.[1]
>
> - Hekigodo

"Of course, the truth is that those autumn leaves in those few glorious days of crimson, scarlet and gold, are not really being discarded.

They are returning to Earth, as we too must some day do. I guess the important thing to remember," Soga continued, "is that we are all part—and only a part—of this universe. Look! Look at those millions of stars. Look at the Milky Way...it is said to be more than billions of stars. How can man think he is a superior being to all other objects in this universe? We are only one part—an important part but only a part—and we must co-exist with billions of other parts. This Earth itself is only an insignificant part of the total universe."

"Are you saying that, seen in that perspective, our being interned is insignificant?"

"Nothing is insignificant. Even the maple leaves falling in autumn is not insignificant. How can I say that tearing a man away from his home and family, his job and his community is insignificant? No, what I am saying is that everything, every action, every object, interlocks. Tennyson, in his poem, wanted to know what life is. Hekigodo, in his poem, merely accepts life. He knows the tree has gone through a cycle. That tree has gone through cycles of beauty—in spring and autumn—and of starkness, in winter. If we can accept that, can we not also accept man in his youth, his manhood, his old age, even his death?

"Soga-san," the Statesider said, "didn't you tell me you were a newspaper editor? I thought newspaper people were very objective. But you are a poet and a philosopher."

Then, "I see you walking along the barbed wire fence every evening. May I join you sometimes?"

CHAPTER 14

MISSOULA:

The 50 Pioneers

Move? Again?

The men were no longer fearful of these moves, but it was bothersome and time-consuming. Besides, they had accumulated various objects such as fossilized rocks and tree aberrations, which they had laboriously sawed, sanded, polished and shellacked, and for which they required additional boxes.

"We move you from time to time to keep you physically and mentally alert," a friendly official told them. "The activity of sorting, packing, cleaning and moving to a new location is challenging, beneficial."

"You mean the American government is concerned about our mental and physical health?"

"Of course. Else why go to the expense of shifting you people from camp to camp?"

"That's a hard one to believe. Thanks for nothing..." the internees bantered. "But we're going to miss officials like you, who understood and were good to us."

They exchanged home addresses, but would they ever write to each other? They were sad, that they had to meet and part under such circumstances.

The Missoula group left on June 2, sitting three days and two nights in the train, but this trip was less tiring than the others because they were allowed to stand and walk around in their own car.

They spent part of the time complaining that they had not been allowed to bring with them the handcrafts they had so lovingly made for their families. These had to be left in the "office," since they were allowed only one suitcase each. But Furuya had wrapped his rattle in tissue paper, then placed it in the pocket of his overcoat for safekeeping. "Oh, I forgot it was there," he practiced saying in a surprised tone, should the officials find it.

Fort Missoula turned out to be a military reservation which had once housed Indians. Always, it seemed, they were sent to Indian reservation outskirts. There was the usual messhall, laundry and showers, but this one had a real theater.

To the southwest was a mountain range. To the east were battlefields where, it is said, the Bitterroot River which ran next to it ran red with blood during the Indian wars. Now there was fish in the clear cold water which flowed from the mountains which were still covered with snow. Wild flowers carpeted the fields, and there were even some purple iris bordering the barracks planted by someone who had lived there earlier. It was a quiet, beautiful place.

To his surprise, Furuya found friends who had left Livingston earlier to return to Japan on the exchange ship *Gripsholm*. Kenji Kimura from Nippon Yusen Kaisha explained sheepishly that he had missed the

Gripsholm although his goods sailed with it. There were also about 500 Italians, Germans and Czechs, but they soon left, and about 120 Japanese from Peru, Bolivia and Nicaragua came. Some were old friends from other camps. Rev. Josen Deme—the "German"—and Masayuki Chikuma—the actor-cook—were there.

The commander, P. H. Fraser, gave them self-rule and each block elected a mayor, vice-mayor, secretary and treasurer. To Furuya's surprise and delight, most of those elected were from Hawai'i. He was pleased that the Hawai'i internees had earned so much respect from the others.

Also, at Missoula, each man regained his own identity. In the days following Pearl Harbor, Furuya had been identified as ISN-HJ-CI 188. For so many months, he had been an impersonal number, like a convict. Well, why not? He had been incarcerated just like a convict.

But now he regained his name and address: Kumaji Furuya, Box 1539, Honolulu, T.H., U.S.A. He felt like a human being again.

Within each dormitory—no longer called barracks—there were 38 to 40 people. Every ten dormitories of about 360 men had their own messhall, showers and latrines. The men cleaned their own dorms, heated the bathwater, and helped with messhall responsibilities. Beyond that, they were free to engage in camp activities.

When the group was settled, the younger men again wanted a golf course, so they got hoe, rake, pick and shovel and constructed a 9-hole course. When the grass grew, the course was almost as beautiful as that at O'ahu Country Club, which did not admit Japanese as members but which they could see from certain parts of Nu'uanu.

Because they raised chickens, they had lots of poultry at the dining table. Chikuma, the cook, had to kill hundreds of chickens a week to feed his compound of 360 men.

One day he was unable to cut a chicken's head off completely, and it went walking off with its head dangling loose at its side. Rev. E. Fujii caught

CAMP MISSOULA: A trimphant baseball team. Left to right, front row: Tomoichi Hayashi, Ryuichi Kashima, Kazumi Matsumoto and Shujiro Takakuwa. Center Row: Masayuki Iwata, Kumaji Furuya, Goki Takiguchi, Yoshinobu Sasaki and Masahiro Himeno. Third row: Soichi Obata, Akio Kimura, Isaku Orita, Tamaki Arita, Masato Kiyozaki and Suijo Kabashima.

Photo Courtesy Kumaji Furuya

sight of it and was horrified. "Chikuma, you're a devil. Why didn't you kill it the first time?"

"But Rev. Fujii, I have to kill hundreds in one hour. Sometimes a chicken moves, and that affects my aim. So I have to chop a second time. This chicken flew away before I could aim a second time."

"Horrible! Horrible! How cruel, to kill a chicken that way."

"But Rev. Fujii, you can't eat a chicken alive. That's what we're raising them for... for food. To eat them, you gotta kill them."

"Horrible! Horrible!" Rev. Fujii repeated, shaking his head and stalking off. He wouldn't eat chicken for several weeks after the incident.

"Have you heard of the saying 'Running around like a chicken without a head?' " Furuya asked Chikuma later.

"Yes. Does it mean you can't see so you're just running around for nothing? Uselessly? Like people who rush around endlessly but don't accomplish anything?"

"Could be...or could it be that our end is a foregone conclusion? Like the chicken without a head, we'll all be dying within our predestined time. Our posturing and pretending, our grandiose dreams, our magnanimous gestures are all in vain. We go when we have to go... But then, we're not chickens. I guess all it means is for us to have dignity, to meditate, to think things through. Instead of running around aimlessly, have a purpose in life."

"I wish I didn't have to be the one to kill the chickens," Chikuma said. "Everyone eats chicken, but no one wants to kill them. One mistake in your aim, and someone gets angry with you."

"Well, Chikuma," Furuya laughed, "you can't say that a chicken with its head dangling on one side and still walking around is an everyday sight. Don't blame Fujii for being so disturbed."

It was getting close to December, so some of the men were given passes to shop in town; a single guard accompanied them, indicating trust. The trees along the mountain roads leading to town were scarlet and gold, and in Missoula itself, a town of about 18,500, willow trees draped green branches over the street, casting a lacy shadow over curbs. It was an indescribably romantic town.

Furuya was surprised at the merchandise in the Missoula Mercantile Store, for he found food, drugs, cosmetics, farm equipment, clothing, sporting goods, recreational supplies and even padded blankets, resembling the futon at home. On the walls were heads of reindeer, wolf, buffalo and other animals, with a plaque to indicate who the hunter had been.

Furuya bought some material and other items to be sent as gifts to his family in Honolulu. The salesgirl asked, "Are you Mexican?"

Here it comes, thought Furuya. "No, I'm Japanese."

"Japanese? Do you live in town?"

"No, we live in a camp a few miles from here. It's an internment center."

"What's that?"

"That's where they keep some of the aliens of those countries against whom the U.S. is fighting this war. Countries like Germany, Italy, Japan…"

"Are you from Japan?"

"No, I'm from Hawai'i."

"But Hawai'i is not our enemy, is it? Why do the Japanese from Hawai'i have to be in an internment camp?"

"That's what we'd like to know," Furuya smiled. His heart was full, as he inwardly blessed her. How wonderful it was, to be treated as just another human being, not an individual tainted with disloyalty.

As the autumn days passed, even the crows began disappearing. One misty twilight, the men saw a sight they had never seen before. The sky above them was black with ducks that cawed their way south.

The next morning those who woke up early and went outside found some ducks had crashed into buildings. Others had been injured, caught on wires. A minister found one, and called it manna from Heaven. They all had duck for dinner that night, but the meat was tough and stringy, unlike their chickens.

The winter chill came early and suddenly. The apple growers in the surrounding area, caught by surprise, asked the camp commander if some of the internees would be willing to help pick apples. The men realized it would be tiring work, but at least it would be something different, so some volunteered. The men left early in the trucks pro-vided, and picked the dark pink, firm and juicy apples all day.

"How come we never see this type of apple in Hawai'i," they asked.

"These bruise easily. And if they're bruised they spoil within a day or two, so they're not good export apples," they were told.

When they returned to camp, they were allowed one paper sack of free apples. A sack held about eight apples. But each man had more than eight friends, and he wanted all of them to taste these apples. So each worker tightened the leggings on the pants, buttoned shirt sleeves and shirt, and filled the space next to the body with apples. Ballooned, they stood like robots or clowns all the way home, for they couldn't sit. But what joy there was at camp, as they distributed an apple to as many men as possible.

The colors and coolness of autumn was soon replaced by frigid winter weather. Some of the men caught cold and were hospitalized for days or weeks. They looked pale and wan, like Japan tourists who used to come to Hawai'i in late February or March. Furuya himself went to the hospital a few days before Christmas and thought he was getting better when, on New Year's Eve, a Catholic priest came and prayed over him. Now why did the priest do that? Were these the "last rites" he had read about in books ? Was he dying and no one was brave enough to tell him? "Tell me the truth," he insisted, but his friends said the hospital wouldn't give them any information regarding patients.

154

Then an orderly brought *mochi, nishime* and *sushi* on New Year's Day. The Japanese food tasted so good, he knew he couldn't be dying. A dying man would not have had such an appetite. He secretly poured his medicine into a potted plant and soon became well enough to return to the dormitory. Because it was cold—32 degrees on January 17, and several degrees below zero at night—the others brought his food from the dining room to the barrack.

It was soon after New Year's Day that the camp received such items as tea, soy sauce, *miso* and Japanese medicine, sent by the Japan Relief Fund through the Red Cross. 50,000 pounds of tea, 8,600 barrels of soy sauce, and 500 tons of books in the Japanese language were delivered to internees in both WRA and Department of Justice camps.

"I guess we're Japanese, after all," the men said. "Even when we're in a camp and Japan is at war and losing, at that, still the Japanese people sacrificed this food for us. To them we are fellow Japanese, and they want to comfort those of us in internment camps." That night they sang *Kimigayo*, the Japanese national anthem, to thank the Japanese people for their sacrifice and thoughtfulness.

But the internees' respect for Americans grew too. One spring day, some of the men were allowed to shop in Missoula. When the purchases had been completed, the men wandered off to a cemetery close by and strolled casually through the grounds glancing at moss-encrusted tombs. Suddenly someone called out, "Look, look! How did a Japanese get here?"

"A Japanese? Buried here? Why, here's another!"

"And here's one..."

In all, they counted 50 graves of Japanese. They had died between 1900 and 1909, about 30 to 40 years ago. Some had emigrated from Hokkaido and Niigata in northern Japan; others had come from warmer Hiroshima and Wakayama. One had been only 18 when he died, another 19. The majority had been in their 20s and 30s, and a few had been from 59 to 63. The name of the person, his date of birth and death, and his *ken*—his province—identified the man buried under each tombstone.

Had they come before the turn of the century to work on the railroads? Why had the 18-year-old and 19-year-old died? Had they not been able to adjust, coming from warm Hiroshima, to work in cold and rugged Montana? What had Montana been like, in the first decade of the 1900s? Had they starved to death? Got caught in an epidemic? Froze during a cold winter? Had the survivors been able to get word to parents in Japan as to what had happened to their beloved sons? Why had so many died in a period of only nine years ? Who had provided for these tombs? Was the last Japanese to die also buried here?

The site of their graves was clean. Someone had mowed the grass, cleared the weeds, and even scrubbed the mold from the tombstone.

Later, 24 priests received permission from the camp commander to hold Buddhist services for the deceased. They burned incense at each grave. Their tears fell, not for the young men who had died without having their dreams realized, but in gratefulness that the town residents had cared for the graves for so many years, and especially now, knowing the ethnic origin of those buried below.

"Those leaders who interned us are Americans," the priests said. "But these Missoula residents are Americans too. These Americans are thoughtful enough to care for graves of unknown people. At home, in Hawai'i, some children neglect to clean around their own parents' gravesite. And here are Americans who have kept these Japanese tombstones clean."

"Yes, the Americans are people with consideration for other human beings. They are human beings first, not Americans or Japanese first."

The cold winter was less cold after that discovery.

CHAPTER 15

FAMILY CAMPS:

Crystal City and Jerome

At the family camp in Crystal City, Texas, activity began when 137 women moved in. They belonged to the diplomatic corps or were wives of wealthy international merchants, and had been at plush Grove Park Inn in North Carolina. They had traveled and lived in luxury, but now they were housed in shacks that had originally been built as a seasonal labor camp for Mexican migrant workers.

Some of these women returned to Japan in September, 1943, but others remained at Crystal City until the end of the war, when they returned to Japan by way of Los Angeles.

In comparison with other internee camps, Crystal City was considered more or less desirable. Residents received 57¢ a day in coupons.

The coupons could be exchanged for whatever food was being sold that day. One day was egg day; one could buy seven eggs per week per person for 2¢ an egg. Other days were catsup days, butter days, meat days, even a tofu day. Rice, flour and other staples were available any day. Since the Japanese women didn't care for butter, and the Germans didn't eat tofu, they bought these and exchanged them at their barracks. The internees could even buy a bottle of Masamune Brand sake or a case of beer a week. Many with large families had coupons left over or their rooms were piled high with various foods.

Despite some overcrowding, life at Crystal City was such that men in other camps made it their objective to get their family into that camp. Some Hawai'i women and even families were also sent there.

Mrs. Haru Tanaka, who had been interned Dec. 7, 1941, was a busy organizer at Crystal City. She was not one to feel sorry for herself, and she didn't want others to continue feeling sorry for themselves, either.

"There's so much work to do, with all these young children needing activities," she said. "They come first."

She remembered how, on Dec. 7, she had been out in her garden from early in the morning, since it was Sunday, a day of rest. She had lost her husband 12 years earlier, and there were two children, so she supplemented her food with homegrown vegetables as much as possible.

That Sunday, she had heard the sharp whine of planes, but she heard them every day, since the area she lived in near Wahiawa adjoined Schofield Barracks and Wheeler Air Force Base. Wahiawa's chief source of income came from the soldiers who poured into town each day from military installations.

"I saw Mr. Takeda, a carpenter, on his way to a bakery to buy fresh pastries, the way he did every Sunday," she recalled. "He had a trenchcoat over his pajamas and zori on his feet."

Takeda went to the bakery only on Sundays, since he left early on other mornings for his carpentry job. That Sunday, he had noticed an unusually large number of planes in the air, and had told the bakery saleswoman, "I don't see why they have to practice on Sundays too." Maneuvers had been going on all week, but surely the Army and Air Force could rest on Sundays!

There was a loud explosion close by, then another. Takeda was furious. The military had no consideration for the residents! What about people who wanted to sleep late on Sundays? It was not yet 8 a.m.

On the way home, he had sat on a low stone wall overlooking the lake, noticing the eucalyptus tree roots made intricate and artistic designs in the shallow water. Instantly he shot up. There, on the wall was a still hot bit of metal.

"Look at this!" he shouted, although no one else was around. "We should notify the police. The military is getting too careless. Someone could get hurt." He picked up the piece of metal with a few green leaves and walked to the police station.

"Look," he fumed. "I almost made a hole in my topcoat."

"Mr. Takeda, what are you doing here," the policeman had answered. He knew just about everyone in Wahiawa.
"Go home...go home...it's dangerous to be out on the streets."

"You bet it's dangerous. Look what I sat on..." He produced the piece of metal.

"Mr. Takeda, don't you know we're being bombed by Japanese planes? Look! Look!"

Takeda looked up. Sure enough, those were Japanese planes, with the sun insignia, streaking for home base, somewhere north of the island.

"Go home, Takeda-san," But Takeda was already running, a wallet and a piece of metal in one hand and the pastries in the other. It was only as he neared his home that he saw a fire in the distance. Whose house was it? Was it Kunihisa's daughter's home? That was a brand new house!

Then he saw it was his own. People were spraying water on their own roofs, trying to prevent flames from jumping to their homes. Saving the Takeda home after a direct hit was impossible. Fire trucks had to come from Schofield Barracks, and by the time they reached Wahiawa, the house would be gutted. The telephone lines were jammed and they couldn't even reach the fire department anyway. Takeda could only stare, until a family friend led him away.

Haru Tanaka had come to convey her shock and condolences. Her mind was working furiously. After all, the FBI had investigated her earlier. They had wanted to know when she had come to Hawai'i, the number of trips she had made to Japan since then, the donations she had made to assist wounded Japanese soldiers from 1939 to 1941, and what her responsibilities were as a part-time Japanese Consulate worker. Also, as a Japanese school teacher, didn't she make the students sing the Japanese national anthem before the beginning of class each day? And didn't the anthem teach loyalty to the Japanese emperor? Patriotism toward Japan?

"We have the students for one hour a day. Many parents think of us more as babysitters than as teachers. The English schools have the children from 8 a.m. to 2:30 p.m. We have them from 3 to 4 p.m. If you think we can teach these children to be patriotic, or even to learn the Japanese language well, you give us too much credit. I doubt if the students know what the words to the national anthem mean."

"You're a part-time agent for the Japanese Consulate. You send in reports. That's spying for the Japanese government."

"Reports? What we report are births, deaths, marriages of Japanese couples. These are then sent to the Japanese village from which an immigrant came, so there is a record of the family even if some Japanese have gone overseas to North or South America. If you visit the village office in Japan, you'll find the genealogy of families dating back many generations. I myself can trace my family back to the late 1700s."

"Why can't each family write back to Japan without going through the Japanese Consulate?"

"Because many of the early immigrants are illiterate. They come to me and tell me verbally who was born when or who died when and I record these dates for my district and send them to the Japanese Consulate. It in turn sends these records back to the villages."

Haru Tanaka was aware that often the record of a birth of a Japanese child could be verified at the Consulate, rather than at the Bureau of Vital Statistics in the Board of Health because the immigrant mother had no one to turn to who could relay such information in English.

The investigators had left, but Haru Tanaka was not one to leave things to chance. As soon as she saw the Japan planes, she packed some essentials, such as comb, toothbrush and toothpaste, handkerchiefs, underwear, Aspirin and pencil and paper. Sure enough, after lunch, four MPs and police had knocked at the door.

"Mrs. Haru Tanaka? Will you come with us? We'd like to ask you a few questions."

"May I change my clothes?"

"Of course." They waited as she went into the bedroom and wore as much as she possibly could, including her overcoat.

Already in the car were Mr. Sekiya and Mr. Hino, who were hand-cuffed. Haru was made to sit on the front seat, without handcuffs.

"Next is Fujii...Kīpapa..." the MP told the driver. Haru Tanaka knew whom they meant. Mr. Fujii was an elementary school teacher. However, he wasn't home.

"Pearl City..." Area after area, they searched for Japanese language school teachers, but many had evacuated their homes in the Pearl Harbor area.

It was almost midnight when they had reached the Immigration Office. They had been riding for several hours, without food, without a rest stop, without being able to talk to one another or to have their questions answered. They had seen unchecked cane fires, but the city was dark.

After being registered, Mrs. Tanaka was ushered into a small room. In the darkness, after she was pushed in with a flashlight, she saw two figures, but she could not recognize them. The next morning she found two priestesses. They bowed good-morning to each other, not realizing they were to be camp mates for the next few years.

And now here she was at Crystal City. But so what? She could teach children here just as well as she could teach them at home.

She immediately set about helping to organize a Japanese language school. Many parents, believing they were all to be sent to Japan, and realizing their children didn't know much, if any, Japanese, enrolled them in Japanese as well as in an English school. Classes were alternated, so as not to have overflow crowds in the morning or afternoon...that is, half the children attended English school in the morning, and the other half attended the Japanese school. In the afternoon, the students changed schools. During the evenings, older children could attend interest classes, such as calligraphy, singing, dancing, painting and culture classes. Haru was too busy to mope about injustices or to question why she had been interned when many other female school teachers had not been.

That first Christmas, a matron gave Haru Tanaka $100 of her own savings. "Please buy something for the children," she said, providing Haru with a pass into town. "They are innocent victims. They must at least have Christmas, the way they did at home." The atmosphere at camp was not an adversary one; they tended to understand their roles.

The following Christmas, the Girl Scouts and Boy Scouts in the surrounding area collected and brought gifts for the camp children. The women at Crystal City separated the gifts for the young by age and sex and wrapped them in Christmas paper. On Christmas Eve, a rather small and thin camp Santa Claus ho-ho-hoed and delivered the gifts.

One observant five-year-old boy caught Santa Claus by the arm and asked, "Santa Claus, how come you have a hole in your shoe? I can see your baby toe through your socks."

Santa Claus looked at his shoe and said, "That's because I'm so busy making gifts for you, I didn't have time to make shoes for myself."

A week later, Santa Claus reached for his old shoes under his cot and found a pair of brand new ones, gift of members at the camp, including the guards!

In August, 1945, after Japan had been defeated, the camp members were told they would be returned to Hawai'i or Japan, whichever they chose.

"It might be November or December when you leave, and it'll be cold on the train and ship. Take your blankets with you. Surely we can spare them," a kind camp official said.

A pro-Japan priest sneered. "Take these dirty blankets? When the Japan ship comes for us, they will bring us clean new blankets. Who wants these ragged old things?" He was absolutely certain Japan had won the war, had ordered the camps closed, and had arranged for the return home to Japan.

But when they reached Los Angeles, there were no Japan ships, no clean blankets. The pro-Japan group was undaunted. "Japan is allowing some American ships to take us back to Hawai'i. Wait till we get to Honolulu. We'll find Japan flags flying all over the city. Then you'll believe Japan won the war," the group's leader insisted.

Some internees were already at Santa Ana Army Airfield Camp to await the army transport *Shawnee* that was to take them home to Hawai'i. Meanwhile, the WRA conducted tours of Los Angeles and its suburbs for the restless internees.

The war had already been over for four months and the Army wanted to return people home as soon as possible, so the *Shawnee* was packed when it sailed.

The promenade sections of A and B decks had been turned into dorms in which 3-decker beds had been installed.

Long tables without benches served as dining tables. Adults and children over six ate standing and only mothers with younger children could be seated in the officers' mess.

On ship which sailed from Wilmington Harbor at 4 p.m. on a 1945 December afternoon were 40 American-Japanese soldiers returning from duty away from Hawai'i. These soldiers, members of the famed 100th Infantry and the 442nd Battalion which had won so many medals and the respect of appreciative Americans, gave assistance to new mothers, the elderly and the ill when and where possible.

Meanwhile, in Hawai'i, another group was meeting to provide assistance to the returning internees and evacuees. Some community leaders were meeting to find housing for incoming families. Of the 500 that had returned from Seattle via the *Yarmouth* and the 580 from Los Angeles via the *Shawnee*, 55 families had lost their housing accommodations while interned. There were also 44 new families electing to come to Hawai'i as new residents, including families from South America that were finding it difficult to return home to that continent. About 88 families comprising 502 individuals or almost half of the total group also indicated they wanted to live on the island of O'ahu, thereby intensifying the already acute housing shortage.

Led by Miss Mildred Towle of the International Institute of the YWCA and joined by representatives of the Hawai'i Housing Authority, the Army, the Emergency Service Committee, the Child and Family Service, and the Swedish Vice Consulate, the group set up a housing committee. One request this group made to alleviate the housing problem on a temporary basis was to have the Army relinquish Holiday House, a former Japanese high school taken over by the Army as an overnight hotel for servicemen. This building, the YMBA, could supply beds for about ten families until more permanent housing could be located and acquired.

Unknown to most internees, there were many in Hawai'i who had worked not only before the war, such as Special Agent for FBI Robert L. Shivers, but during and after the war to ease the return of the internees to the islands. But so quietly was work done that few realized what was taking place in meeting rooms around the city. These groups did not stop at vague promises; they acted in various ways to alleviate more suffering and to diminish the bitterness of the internees.

But in the fall of 1942, two frightened children had clung to their mother.

"Mama, where are we going? " seven-year-old June Hoshida asked.

"To meet Daddy," her mother answered. "In a place called Jerome, Arkansas."

"Sandy, did you hear that? We're going to Daddy," June hugged her two-year-old sister, who was wrapped around one of her mother's legs.

Mrs. Hoshida, carrying the three-month-old baby Carole, drooped with exhaustion. She had been in line with over a hundred people, waiting to be assigned to a bus, to go to wherever they were taking the women and children. It was difficult even to stand, let alone walk, with the baby in her arms and Sandra hanging on to her skirt or legs. Tears streamed down her face.

"Mommy, mommy, don't cry. Did we do something bad?" June asked, juggling the bag of diapers, medicine, baby food and other necessities in her tiny arms.

"Oh, June, no! No! You are such a good girl, to help Mommy carry the bag. I'm crying because I'm tired, that's all. Aren't you tired too? As soon as we get to where we're going to sleep tonight, I can put Carole down, feed her, and clean her. I'll be alright then."

But it wasn't that easy. First she had to line up to get on the boat that took her from the island of Hawai'i to the island of O'ahu. Then she had to line up to get off the boat. Now she was lining up to get on the bus. Soon she was to line up to be registered at the Immigration Station where they were perhaps to sleep that night, a group of weeping mothers and squalling babies.

Within a few days she would have to line up to be checked out of the Immigration Station, line up to board the bus that was to take them to the ship, then line up to board the ship.

About ten days later, she would have to line up again to get off the ship in San Francisco, to board the ferry to go to Angel Island, then for the train which would take them to Jerome Relocation Center.

At each line she felt she would drop from the exhaustion, with the baby crying in her arms and Sandra adding her weight, making it difficult even to stand. But when she saw June, only seven, carrying the heavy bag and trying to comfort Sandra, she felt she had to be strong. Besides, the other women were undergoing the same ordeal. There was Mrs. Otojiro Ozaki, with her young children. There was Mrs. Shigeo Fujino, with her baby. And anyway, this ordeal would be over when she reached the Relocation Center. George would be waiting to share some of the burden. The officials in Hawai'i had promised her she could be with her husband. It was a matter of a few days more.

She had one pleasant memory. While in Honolulu, she had been able, through a special request, to visit her daughter Taeko at the Waimano Home. Taeko had been placed there because it would have been impossible to transport her to a Mainland relocation center.

When she had been led into the room where eight-year-old Taeko lay motionless in her crib, for she was too tiny to require a bed, she whispered, "Taeko…"

Instantly the unseeing eyes opened, a smile broke on the pale face, and the one good hand flew into the air for the intertwining of fingers it sought.

"Taeko, Taeko," Mrs. Hoshida wept. "Taeko, I'm sorry I had to put you in here. There's a war going on…I told you that before, didn't

I? I know you don't know what a war is, but Daddy was taken far away...that's why he hasn't come to talk to you...and now we must go and join him. We don't have a home anymore...we had to give up your home...we don't have any money. I can't work with Carole and Sandra and June. So I have to go where Daddy is. That is why we have to leave you here. But Taeko, as soon as the war is over, and we come back to Hawai'i, we will come for you. June and Sandra will play with you again. Do you understand, Taeko?"

Mrs. Hoshida knew Taeko didn't understand, but that didn't matter. "Taeko, we'll be back some day, so you wait for us, OK? We all love you. We'll think of you every day."

Taeko moved her lips, but no sound emerged. The child could only express her happiness at hearing her mother's voice by clinging to her mother's hand.

"Maybe I could get a job in Honolulu...I heard there are lots of war jobs now...and I could visit you every Sunday," Mrs. Hoshida said. But with three small children, no particular work skills, and her frail body, who would hire her? And if they did, who would care for the children? Could she keep up? No, her only alternative was to be reunited with her husband, for the sake of the other three children.

"Taeko, *ganbatte neh*?" she whispered as she untangled Taeko's tiny fingers from her own. "I will *ganbaru* so you must *ganbaru* too..."

Mrs. Hoshida and the other women boarded the *Lurline*, now painted a dark grey, and descended the steep steps to the bottom of the ship, much as her husband must have done. But with the baby in her arms, and Sandra still clinging to her dress, it was doubly or triply more difficult. And once in the cabin, she found it difficult to sleep, for Sandra insisted on sleeping with her on the narrow cot, still entwined to her mothers' leg. How frightened she must be...so afraid she might lose me in this huge crowd, her mother thought, and whispered in

Sandra's ear, "Don't be frightened, Sandra. Mommy will not lose you."

But why shouldn't Sandra be frightened, with the pushing, the hundreds of drawn faces, crying babies, shouting officials, and unfamiliar places?

Soon we will be in Jerome, she whispered, as much to herself as to Sandra, and Daddy will take Carole from my arms. Then I'll hold you in my arms, Sandra, and you needn't be frightened any more. Soon...soon...soon...soon... soon...soonah...the ship's engine and the train wheels seemed to repeat as they made their way east.

Mrs. Hoshida reached Jerome on January 5, 1943, in freezing weather. Once they had stopped at a station...it said New Mexico... and her heart jumped. Maybe George and the other men would be getting on here so they could help their wives! But she waited in vain. The train began and the next stop was Jerome, Arkansas.

Again they had to line up for the buses that were to take them to the camp. She waited at the station till the last minute for George, but there was no sign of her husband or of any other woman's husband. Reluctantly she boarded a bus.

The officials at Jerome sighed at the sight of the bedraggled lot of women and so many babies, inadequately dressed for Arkansas' winter weather.

"First, find the room in the barracks assigned to you. Then go to the storeroom across the block and get your bedding. You will find cots in the barracks, but you must pick up your blankets and pillows. Later, you will be provided a broom and other household supplies. And it is freezing cold, so see that woodpile? Over there? The wood is for your heater. The fire will keep you warm."

Get your own bedding? Your own firewood? Tears streamed down her cheeks as she asked June to remain with Carole and Sandra in the strange, cold and empty room. She sat Sandra on the cot, but Sandra immediately tumbled off and hung on to her mother's dress.

"Stay, Sandra," she scolded. "I'm just going to get some blankets to keep us warm." But Sandra followed her in the mud to the bedding storeroom and back, storeroom and back, hindering her mother's footsteps.

Then it was to the woodpile and back, woodpile and back, with muddy Sandra still clinging to her coat, eyes wide with fright and too numb to even cry. Then, how to start a fire when she didn't even have newspapers or a match?

Luckily, a man who lived close by went from barrack to barrack to start the stoves for the helpless women. Then Mrs. Hoshida took the muddy shoes and clothes off, made the beds, fed the baby, and settled the children close to the stove. The wood was not too dry, so there was smoke and it was difficult to breathe. Even the lumber for the building must have been green, for they had shrunk, leaving gaps which allowed the damp cold air to seep in. There were no newspapers to wedge in the cracks, so all night she poked at the fire and wept tears of frustration, exhaustion and disappointment that George had not been there to help.

But tomorrow...surely tomorrow George would be here to help care for Carole, comfort Sandra, and praise June. Surely he could fill in the cracks in the wall, carry wood for the fire, and complete the endless official papers they were supposed to read and sign. It was only one more night... one more night after nightmarish days, and they would be reunited.

Tomorrow. "Go to a Mainland WRA camp, and you can be reunited with your husband," the women had been promised in their home town.

It was over a year before Mrs. Hoshida was reunited with her husband!

It was also over a year before Mrs. Hoshida's many acquaintances from Hilo, Hawai'i, including Irene Kanno and Tsuruye Koide, would be reunited with their husbands, Tomio and Kiyoichi.

"I think I can be released earlier if I apply for a parole," Tomio Kanno wrote to Irene. "Then I can join you in Jerome."

"But what is your crime, that you must have a parole on your record, like a jailbird?" Irene wrote back. "Won't they allow me to go there, to your camp?"

"No, this is a camp for men only. There are no children or babies here. In fact, we haven't seen a child for two years now. And the few women we see are Mexicans working in the hospital or office. Since you can't come here, I should apply for Jerome."

Each letter took months to reach its destination because of the time-consuming censoring. By the time they had agreed on a move, all the family men in Camp Lordsburg were scheduled to be relocated to Crystal City, Texas, or Jerome, Arkansas.

When Irene had first reached Jerome in January, 1943, she had been assigned to Block 39, 2F. But unlike Mrs. Hoshida, she refused to walk in the freezing dark to the distant woodpile since there was no one to watch her infant baby. Her frightened five-year-old might venture out in search of her mother. So she dressed them warmly, wrapped blankets around them, and hugged them, one on each side of her.

Within a few days, their skin scaled off, their lips cracked, and they slipped again and again on the icy path as they walked to the messhall. The soles of their sandals were smooth.

"Mama, my feet hurt even with three pairs of socks," Irene's daughter sobbed.

"I know...I know. We shouldn't be wearing sandals in this kind of weather, but I didn't know we'd be coming to such a cold place. I'll order some shoes for you from the Montgomery Ward catalogue as soon as I can borrow one, but it might be a month before we get the shoes."

Irene thought back to 1941. She and her husband had gone on an extended visit to Japan, she explained to Mrs. Koide, Mrs. Yasuro Kurita and the others in the warm messhall where they lingered as long as they could because the children could play with others.

"We visited in Japan from April 1940 to July, 1941, taking movies.

JEROME, ARKANSAS: March, 1944, internee carpenters help build a gymnasium. Left to right, front row: George Y. Hoshida, Kawanishi, Yasuro Kurita, Tomizo Kanno, Kiyoichi Koide and Rev. Takeo Miura. Back row: Kawamura, Tanaka, Arita.

Photo Courtesy George Y. Hoshida

We got out on one of the last ships to leave Japan. Back in Hilo, we were able to get an FHA loan and we built a two-story three-bedroom home with space for a basement downstairs. Our second daughter was born. My husband had a good job with S. Hata Dry Goods and Grocery. He was to be the manager of their new sake division. Things were going so well I asked my husband, "Do you think this luck will hold? Is all this too good to be true?"

On February 9, 1942, the FBI had come for Tomio Kanno and sent him to Sand Island, then to Lordsburg in New Mexico. And Irene wondered what would happen if she broke a leg or developed pneumonia. Who would care for the five-year-old and the infant? She chose to go to Jerome where she was promised she could be with her husband.

The Hawai'i women could not relate to the Mainland women. "What do you think of them?" Irene once asked. "They seldom smile or talk about their children. They register for every class offered. They go to all the meetings, and I notice they listen to everything said. They seem to want to know everything."

"Yes, they don't seem to have the warmth of Hawai'i women," another agreed.

One day the Mainlanders asked the Hawai'i women and children to come to lunch an hour early.

"What kind of meeting is this?" the Hawai'i women grumbled. "The nerve! Why didn't they let us know earlier?" However, they all went because the messhall was warmer than their own barracks.

To their surprise—even shock—they found the Mainlanders had collected sturdy shoes of many sizes, knitted gloves, heavy socks, woolen pants and shirts, scarves, baby blankets and booties. There was worn but warm body-hugging underwear. There were even some overcoats with warm lining.

"Some of us had two overcoats, so we're sharing one with you. Also, our babies and children have more clothes than they really need,

CAMP JEROME: Internees cut trees, then chopped them into firewood for winter use.

Photo Courtesy Irene Kanno

and your children aren't adequately dressed. You can order from Montgomery Ward or Sears, but it takes time for the merchandise to reach here, and your children might catch pneumonia before then."

The Hawai'i women were astonished. They could only stare numbly at the pile of clothes.

"By next winter our husbands may be here," the Mainlanders continued. "They can plug cracks in the walls. They can build a shed so we can pile firewood next to the barracks. We can buy coal, which can keep us warm all night. But until then, try to keep the children healthy, since we don't have adequate medical facilities here. We have a few doctors among us, but they're so overworked."

The Hawai'i group was flabbergasted. Finally someone said, "How can we pay you? We don't have much money." "Why should you pay us? We're just sharing what we have. Besides, when the war ends, and we can return to our homes, we..."

The temporary softness of the Mainland women disappeared. The stern, stifled look returned.

"We're from California," a woman volunteered. "Our husbands are internees, just as yours are...not evacuees. Had we been evacuees, we'd have been together with our husbands. As it is, our husbands are in Bismarck, North Dakota..."

"We had a few weeks before we were sent here... to settle accounts, to pack...Our children went to the city authorities," another woman broke in. "Yes, the authorities told us, we could store our goods in our church while we were away. We had been good citizens, so he would see to it that our church building was policed carefully. The church is a holy place. No one would desecrate it. Our goods would be safe there."

"So we moved the church pews to the side, against the windows. We put our carefully wrapped pianos and organs in, our refrigerators, washers and dryers, our bookcases with family albums and rare books, our bureaus with treasured kimonos and wedding gowns. The young

174

ones barricaded the doors and windows from the inside and triple-locked the heavy front door."

"My albums—grandma's picture in her wedding attire—" a woman whispered. "The brocaded obi! This was the only item Grandma wouldn't sell even when we were starving. 'This is a family heirloom. It was passed on to me. And I am passing it on to you, and you must do the same to your grandchildren,' she had told me. A church... at least a church...would be safe, we had thought, but..."

"Do you know what happened?" an anguished woman wept. "We heard looters couldn't get in so they burned the church down. What wasn't burned was looted. For the refrigerators and washing machines they burned our pianos, our kimonos, our family albums which can never be reproduced..."

The Hawai'i women felt small. Here they had been gossiping about the Mainland women, claiming they were stern and cold. Now they realized the Mainlanders were trying to swallow their bitterness and pain without too many tears. They were enduring their helplessness and anger without emotional outbursts. It was what the Japanese called *nasakenai* and *kurushii*...no American words could describe these feelings. A smile could not come easily when their past had been wiped out vengefully, and the future was a world of hatred and unacceptance.

The Hawai'i women wept in their own barracks for the Mainlanders' grief.

CHAPTER 16

THE WELFARE OF THE FAMILY:

FBI-Nemesis and Savior

The Hawaiian community's concern for the internees, their families, and the community itself began long before the first internee was picked up on Dec. 7, 1941.

Masaji Marumoto, then a young lawyer and later a Supreme Court justice, happened to sit at a dinner table with FBI Special Agent Robert L. Shivers aboard the passenger ship *Nitta Maru* on May 26, 1940. The next day Shivers called Marumoto to invite him to the FBI offices in Dillingham Building in the business district. Shivers explained that he was being bombarded with anti-Japanese information and wanted contacts with the Japanese community so he could judge the Japanese himself. Thereupon Marumoto hosted a dinner party at his home for four other AJA couples and the Shiverses. Later, the Japanese Chamber of Commerce sponsored a cocktail reception so that top Army and Navy officers could meet Japanese community leaders. Other meetings, both small and of mass groups, were subsequently held. Involved were General Short, Admiral Kimmel, and government and business executives.

Shivers formed two advisory groups, one the Committee for Inter-Racial Unity in Hawai'i, and the other the O'ahu Citizens Committee for Home Defense.

In December, 1940, Shivers phoned Hung Wai Ching, the first Asian executive secretary of the University of Hawai'i's YMCA, to ask if he could attend a Dec. 16 meeting at the prestigious Pacific Club. He asked if Ching could advise the FBI on how to handle the community in the event of hostilities with Japan. Shivers wanted to preserve racial harmony among the local Filipinos, Chinese and Koreans whose native lands in Asia were already being overrun by Japanese military forces. The Committee for Inter-Racial Unity in Hawai'i was developed after this meeting.

Members of this Committee included insuranceman Masatoshi Katagiri, educator Shigeo Yoshida, Col. Fielder of Army Intelligence, Capt. Mayfield of Navy Intelligence and Robert L. Shivers, acting as chairman.

Shivers also formed a second committee—the O'ahu Citizens Committee for Home Defense—with Shunzo Sakamaki as chairman. This Committee monitored what took place in the Japanese community, encouraged loyalty to the U.S., and sought to prepare the general public psychologically for the probability of war with Japan.

Membership in this Committee at one time or another included Masaji Marumoto, Mitsuyuki Kido, Shigeo Yoshida, Masatoshi Katagiri, Ralph Honda, Thomas Kurihara, Shigeo Soga, Uichi Kanayama and some others who met once a week. Some of this group were breakfasting at the Shivers' home on Sunday, Dec. 7, when the news of Pearl Harbor was received.

The Territory of Hawai'i formed still another committee on Dec. 11, 1941, a few days after Pearl Harbor. Called the Public Morale

Section of the Territorial Office of Civilian Defense, the members consisted of one Caucasian, one Chinese American, and one Japanese American. These were Charles F. Loomis, Hung Wai Ching, and Shigeo Yoshida. The primary functions of the members were to act as liaisons for racial and national groups on questions and adjustment relating to war, and to promote activities designated to sustain community morale and national unity.

Under the broad umbrella of the Public Morale Section were several sub-committees, including the Emergency Service Committee, created February 8, 1942, to work with the Japanese community. Appointed members, many of whom worked on other committees, were Masaji Marumoto, Shigeo Yoshida, Masatoshi Katagiri, Y. Baron Goto, Dr. Ernest Murai, and Dr. Katsumi Kometani. Executive secretary was Mitsuyuki Kido.

Because of the early intercommunication and interaction between Hawai'i's people, the military forces and the FBI, the Japanese in Hawai'i fared better than West Coast Japanese, even though Hawai'i was closer to Japan with many military installations making it more strategically located. The need for Japanese labor in Hawai'i's economic system, since the Japanese comprised about one third of the total population, played a role in keeping Japanese Americans in the islands, but the trust built up between the Intelligence forces—FBI, Army, and Navy—and the Japanese community contributed significantly to the support received by the Japanese from military leaders.

Robert L. Shivers was later to testify before a Congressional Committee that the Japanese cooperated with and assisted in the promotion of the war effort.

> There was not a single act of sabotage in the Hawaiian Islands during the course of the entire war. Nor was there any fifth-column activity in existence or in evidence here...nowhere under the sun could there have

> been a more intelligent response to the needs of the
> hour than was given by the entire population in these
> islands... including the cooperation of the Japanese
> group and the valuable assistance given by certain
> members of this group, not only to the FBI but to the
> intelligence services of both Army and Navy.[1]

Such assistance and cooperation did not happen by chance. The total community's reaction required early planning and action, and accurate evaluation of people's loyalties in the event of a war.

The first internee was picked up Dec. 7, and the first boatload of internees was sent to the Mainland on February 20, 1942.

By March 31, 1942, the American Red Cross had met and issued a "Statement of Procedure in Connection with the Providing of Welfare Service to the Dependents of Internees and Detained Persons." Its purpose was to mobilize community resources to "prevent suffering and want among certain families and their dependents through sympathetic consideration of their needs" and "to build the morale of these persons to help them maintain a useful place in the civilian community."[2] The Summary included the following procedures:

> Cases involving need of financial assistance would be
> referred to the Department of Public Welfare. Cases
> involving family problems would be referred to the
> Child and Family Service. Cases involving severe emo-
> tional problems would be referred to agencies such as
> the American Friends Service Committee, Emergency
> Service Committee of the Morale Section of the Office
> of the Military Governor, and the Bureau of Mental
> Hygiene.[3]

On April 24, 1942, the Federal Security Agency of the Social Security Board, Bureau of Public Assistance, issued a "Summary of

Program for Providing Necessary Assistance to Enemy Aliens and Other Persons Affected by Restrictive Action of the Federal Government." That summary stated:

> The basis for assuming Federal responsibility for this program is the recognition that the relief of distress caused by restrictive action of the Federal government against enemy aliens necessary to protect the public welfare and the progress of the war effort is a governmental responsibility. These instructions are specifically directed toward individual situations in which the need experienced by enemy aliens and other persons and their families or dependents arises from the restrictive action taken by appropriate governmental authority, such as compulsory removal and relocation, or detention or internment.[4]

The regional public assistance representative of the Social Security Board was authorized to assure State agencies of reimbursement for expenditures made under the program. Records of assistance were to be kept to provide a basis for claiming reimbursement from Japan after the war.

Then, on June 1, 1942, the following agencies met to provide one consistent Summary of Procedure in Providing Assistance to Internee Families: The American Red Cross, Child and Family Service, Social Security Board, Honolulu Council of Social Agencies, American Friends Service Committee, Department of Public Welfare, and Emergency Service Committee.[5]

By December, 1942, when the first contingent of wives and children of internees was sent to Relocation camps on the Mainland, the Department of Public Welfare had provided financial assistance to some 500–600 dependents of about 300 internees. Assistance amounted to about $75,290.[6] After 1942, federal funds of the War Assistance

Program became available to enemy aliens and others affected by governmental actions.

The Spanish government was named as the nation to protect the interests of interned Japanese aliens. But in the Territory of Hawai'i, the Swedish Vice-Consulate represented Japanese interests. Gustav W. Olson was appointed by the Legation at Sweden in Washington, D.C. to act for the Swedish government in the handling of matters concerning Japanese nationals. Its office replaced the Japanese Consulate on Nu'uanu Avenue in Honolulu.

Actually, the bulk of the work involved in protecting Hawai'i's Japanese was carried out by Shimeji Ryusaki, secretary to the Vice-Consul, and her staff of workers. Shimeji had been a McKinley High School retailing coordinator for Hawai'i's Department of Public Instruction. She began serving as liaison between the civilian Japanese in Hawai'i, especially the aliens, and the government. She spoke Japanese and showed compassion for the many who came to the Consulate desperately seeking help.

The Consulate had complete biographical data on Japanese nationals which was provided to military intelligence when requested. But the major task of the Consulate was to provide guidance to Japanese aliens and to assist families left with little or no funds. Shimeji chan-neled cases requiring financial aid to the Department of Public Welfare, and in general followed the Summary outlined by the Red Cross and the other agencies.

Some families refused welfare. In the eyes of many Japanese, welfare was a disgrace that could never be erased. For these families she sought piece jobs, such as sewing, that could be done at home. Steven S. Suzuki, who operated a shirt manufacturing company, was one of those who purposely parceled out such jobs so the women could earn money with dignity.

Shimeji also checked ships transporting prisoners of war and internees—the stories of men locked in their rooms for ten days and allowed out only once every three hours despite strict censorship, had somehow reached Hawai'i. Shimeji thus made sure ships carried medical, reading, and recreational supplies. And, before the women and children left Hawai'i, she would talk to them to acquaint them with procedures and expectations.

The Consulate also arranged for the protection of property left by those deceased for final settlement and disposition at a later date. Such property was held by the Alien Property Custodian.

Also involved in issues concerning the personal property of the Japanese—all alien Japanese, whether interned or not—was the alien property custodian of the Hawaiian Ordnance Depot. This custodian was different from the Custodian who had jurisdiction of productive assets of aliens. The Hawaiian Ordnance Depot custodian was in charge of impounded property which was to be held for the duration of the war. Such impounded property was to be returned eventually, except to those who chose to be repatriated to Japan, who thus forfeited their property.

Under a General Order, all aliens were required to turn in such articles as cameras, short-wave radio receiving sets, fireworks, and implements of war. The Signal Corps made a house-to-house search in areas of Japanese concentration, picking up contraband articles. Large items such as sampans were confiscated and used as landing craft during the war, and in some cases were lost in action. Binoculars and telescopes were used by the Navy. Fireworks were utilized in jungle training centers to simulate war conditions.

Actually many of the items impounded were never reclaimed. Many families had lost their receipts during the four years of war. Those items reclaimed were often "frozen" or rusted beyond repair. The large, more expensive items, such as sampans, were often simply "lost," or there were no records that these items had been confiscated.

In real estate, to prevent takeover by the federal government, directors of Japanese schools hastened to transfer title of their land and buildings to local organizations. The Kaimukī Japanese Language School turned over 35,000 square feet of land and four buildings on

10th Avenue in Honolulu to the YMCA. The McCully Japanese Language School transferred three large buildings and 62,000 square feet at Pumehana and Citron Streets to the City and County of Honolulu. The Mōʻiliʻili School land and buildings were donated to the Mōʻiliʻili Community Association; Kalihi and Wahiawā schools were transferred to the YMCA. Japanese organizations with money in the bank hastened to transfer their funds to non-Japanese organizations.

Unlike the West Coast Japanese, the majority of Hawaiʻi Japanese were spared heartbreak and misery. For this, they could owe thanks to FBI Agent Robert L. Shivers, both their nemesis and their savior. He was their nemesis, for his was the final decision on whether an individual would be interned or not. But he was also their savior, and few realized until much later the effects his legwork in the year before Pearl Harbor had in allaying the fears of the military.

Instead of focusing on what the Japanese "might" or "could" do in the way of sabotage, as the West Coast military powers did, Hawaiʻi's military focused on what the Japanese—aliens and citizens alike—could contribute to the war effort. This focus was possible only because the military—through their intelligence arm and with the assistance of the FBI—had done their homework with a positive frame of mind—that is, the Japanese were to be considered innocent until proven guilty. These initiatives by Shivers especially, in planning ahead to bind the community and the military together paid high dividends both financially and in good will.

CAMP HONOULIULI

CHAPTER 17

HONOULIULI:

Camp for American Citizens

Hana tsumu nobe ni
Hi wa ochite
Minnade kata wo kumi nagara
Uta wo uttatta kaeri michi

Osana najimi no
Ano tomo kono tomo
Aah, dareka kokyo wo
Omowazaru.

In the meadow we picked flowers.
Darkness fell
And arm in arm
We sang as we walked home.

Our childhood friends...
This friend...that friend...
Aah, tonight someone is
Remembering his childhood days.

- Koga Masao

The men sitting on long benches at equally long tables sighed. Those childhood days had been such innocent, carefree, happy days! How much enjoyment the simplest of acts had been: eating *musubi*—rice balls—in a cherry grove or sprawled in a sun-splashed meadow in spring; jumping into a fern shrouded pool on a hot summer day; glorying in the scarlet and orange leaves of autumn; even frolicking naked in the two-foot high snow after a hot, hot, very hot *furo* (bath).

"Urata-san," someone on one of the benches called, "play something else. *Dareka Kokyo Wo Omowazaru*...is too sad...brings back too many childhood memories. How about *Meigetsu Akagi Yama?*"

The men were clad only in their cotton undershirts and undershorts, yet they were perspiring. The day's heat waves were trapped in the camp area because of the hills surrounding it. Located on the "leeward" side of O'ahu, where rain seldom fell, the camp was arid and hot. The sugarcane fields which bordered the dusty road leading from the village of Honouliuli to the camp was kept green with water channeled through the mountain by Waiāhole Tunnel. The water came from the "windward," or rainy side of the island, and the tunnel, the internees had heard, had been dug by early Japanese laborers who had bored through the steep mountain range with rather primitive equipment.

Minoru Urata and his friend Kotaro Taira tuned their guitars, but the nostalgia, the homesickness of the men hung like a shroud over them.

"Tomorrow...let's sing again tomorrow night."

The men reluctantly left the messhall to return to their humid barracks. They did not mind the barbed wire fences or watchtowers with armed guards. Instead, they cursed the engineers who had originally selected this spot as a site for army barracks. *Jigoku-dani*, the internees called the camp. Yes, it was as hot as it must be in *jigoku*, or hell.

Honouliuli Camp, so far as internment camps were concerned, was not a bad camp. The warden, Captain Siegfried Spillner, was fair and impartial. The staff was in general kind and thoughtful, and the men

CAMP HONOULIULI: Located on the island of O'ahu, Honouliuli housed chiefly Japanese-Americans. The long building at right center was messhall and front left buildings served as office and dispensary. Tents in the back served as POW living quarters.

Photo Courtesy Honolulu Advertiser.

were impressed with Sgt. Heen, Sgt. Loveless, Capt. David Dingeman, and Lts. Burger, DeCentes and Fuchero. There was a "no fraternization" rule, but secretly internees and guards helped one another. Sometimes a sergeant had to guard his father's employer; one officer found his uncle in the German compound. In fact, Capt. Carl Eifler found a prospective guard whose father was interned at Sand Island.

"I could never ask a guard to watch over his own father," Eifler said, and transferred the soldier to another company.

Once Minoru Urata refused to work cutting trees, a job which paid 10¢ an hour. The guard threatened him with "That's an order!"

"How about asking Lt. Burger what my rights are," Urata insisted.

"You're a Jap prisoner, a Jap internee, and you do as we command," the guard, newly arrived in Hawai'i, answered.

Lt. Burger upheld Urata. "If he doesn't want to work, he doesn't have to and we can't force him," Burger explained. "To cook, clean the premises, do the laundry... yes. But not outside work where we pay the men. There are some here from wealthy homes who haven't worked at a labor job a single day."

"We pamper them too much," the young guard growled.

"But what have these particular men done that we should punish them?"

"They're the enemy..."

"No, they're not. They're Japanese Americans—American citizens—and their crime is that they attended school in Japan in their youth, as with the four Kageura brothers, or they're in business with firms in Japan, as with Shinzaburo Sumida."

"But what about Pearl Harbor?"

"What about it? These people knew nothing about that. Let's not blame them for what Japan's military strategists did."

"Then what are we holding them for?"

"Well, interning some of them will keep the others from doing things they shouldn't do. Acts as sort of a deterrent."

"Gee whiz! What do we need guards for anyway?" The young soldier saluted and stomped out without a glance at Urata.

In many ways Honouliuli was preferable to Mainland Department of Justice camps. In time the men were allowed visits from family members and friends if the total group behaved itself.

"Listen," newcomers were told, "we're allowed visitations. But if even one person gets into a fight, all visitations are off. You know how we wait to see our families once a month, and if anyone gets into a fight and we don't get to see our wives and children, you know how we're going to treat the one that got into a fight. If you have problems, ask your barrack leader for help. He will contact your captain and the captain will discuss the problem with the camp 'commander,' who is Kaname Murakami."

"Koga, how about playing the samisen for us," Urata asked his barrack mate Masao Koga, who had the same name as a noted Japanese song composer. Koga, a vice-principal at Chuo Gakuin, a Japanese language high school, was a skilled player of the Japanese *samisen*.

"It's late. I might disturb the others. Honda, why don't you tell us about your experiences when you flew in the China War? You've had such an exciting life."

"You mean when we attacked Chungking?" he laughed and looked at Tokuichi Takahashi, who was nicknamed "Chungking" because he looked Chinese.

"No war stories. No stories of atrocities at this time of night," Yamamoto ordered, pounding on the table, then smiling. Again the others laughed. They had started calling Yamamoto "Gombei" after one of Japan's prime ministers because this Yamamoto looked like and began acting like Japan's Yamamoto Gombei.

"Any story...any story..." demanded the others, who were Genpachi Tsushima, a reporter for the Japanese daily *Nippu Jiji*; Tameto Kuramoto and Nobutaro Harada.

"I can tell you about the cold in Manchuria," Honda said. "It was so cold in that vast desert and no coal to keep the homes warm that a few people died every day during the winter months. A truck went around once a week to pick up the bodies."

"You mean they kept the bodies in the house for a week?"

"No, they left the bodies outside in the snow. It would remain frozen until picked up by the truck."

"There you go, pulling our leg again with such stories."

"You think so? We're talking about areas in the world where food is so scarce, female babies are purposely left to die at birth. We're talking about areas where the elderly, when they can no longer contribute to the family, walk out into a blizzard; their bodies may not be found till the following spring. In cultures such as these, dying within a home with family members close by is a luxury few, especially women, can afford. I...we...the Japanese...thought we could change this if we could develop new industries, a new way of life..."

Honda looked at the others. He shook his head. How could anyone imagine what life was like on that frozen steppe if he had not seen those people, eking out a life with a few animals on permafrost land? How could they, when they didn't even believe there could be a land where, if you dug eight to twelve inches below the surface, there was a solid, permanent floor of ice?

"We don't want to hear your bizzare stories, Honda. At least not at this time of night. Your stories are horrid. You told us once it is so cold in Manchuria, when a person urinates, the urine forms a diagonal icicle. How can you make up a disgusting story like that"

"But it's not disgusting," Honda insisted. "We tend to think of urine and feces as dirty. But in cold areas they use the feces of animals for firewood. In India, they use cow dung for firewood. Are you going to say that's disgusting? In Japan we use human waste as fertilizer; is that disgusting?"

Honda looked at those who would not believe his anecdotes. How lucky they were that they lived a life so fortunate such stories were beyond belief!

A few huts away, Tadao Kageura, one of four brothers interned at Honouliuli "talked story" with Masaru Urata, the guitar-playing Urata's cousin, and Seishiro Okazaki, a masseur, who was later to massage Gov. John Burns' wife daily, after she contracted polio. In payment for his gentle patient massage, the Governor was to name his son John Seishiro Burns, although his son did not have a drop of Japanese blood in him. This son was later to become a judge in Hawai'i's courts.

The four Kageura brothers were part of seven sons. Their father had taken them to Japan in 1927, just before the Depression. The children attended school there, as was required. But as they grew older and as impending war darkened Japan's future, the children returned to Hawai'i. First it was Masaichi. Then, in 1936, after nine years in Japan, it was Tadao, then 19. Nobuo returned in 1937 and Yutaka followed soon after.

"In 1939 I got my 'greetings' from the U.S. Army," Tadao told the others. "I passed my physical, so I had a party, at which time I received gifts of money. I was told to be brave, to fight for my country, but not to be foolish and throw my life away. I was primed to fight for my country."

Tadao reported to Schofield Barracks, only to be told he was being rejected because of high blood pressure.

"But they examined me, and I was accepted into the Army," Tadao insisted.

"They weren't thorough enough. This is for your sake, Mr. Kageura, not only for ours," he was told.

"You can't imagine how embarrassed I was," Tadao continued. "I had had a party and I had received gifts of money. Was I to return them or not?"

He returned to his old job at Western State Grocery. "I was there when war broke out. I believed I was a necessary worker in a food-oriented business, and our store was a branch of Theo. H. Davies, and you know that was a big, international outfit."

To his surprise, the FBI came knocking at his door. "I remember that day so clearly," he recalled. "For the first time in my years I was sick and I had gone to the doctor. The FBI said to pack enough clothes for three days, and I wanted to ask them, 'Incuding today?' because my doctor's note was good for three days, counting the day I had gone to the doctor. If I went back to work later than that, I would have had to get another note." He laughed. "I needn't have worried. I haven't been able to report back to the company for two years."

"You know, I coughed and coughed that night. I was sleeping near a window that didn't have glass, only a screen, and it was cold. The next day I went to see a doctor and he gave me two Aspirin."

The others chuckled. "Me too. They give Aspirin for every illness. From a scratch on the leg to cancer…"

"But don't blame Dr. Uchida," Yoshio Akizaki who was interned in the same room as his son Takeo said. "I understand that's all the medicine Dr. Uchida and Capt. Spillner are given."

"Maybe the company that makes Aspirin donated all their old or outdated Aspirin to the Army…By the way do any of you have Bull Durham left?"

In another barrack was Nobuo Kageura, Tadao's brother, and in still another hut was Yutaka, the teenager, and Chojiro. The only one left at home was Masaichi, and he kept away from his brothers for he didn't want to be noticed. After all, someone had to care for the brothers' belongings, and Masaichi was married and had to support a wife.

It was the youngster Yutaka who was to be sent to Tule Lake in

WARDEN OF THE HONOULIULI CAMP: Internees thought high-ly of Captain Siegfried Spillner whom they considered kind and thoughtful.

Photo Courtesy/ Private Collection Siegfried H. Spillner, UH-Mānoa

California for stating he would not volunteer for combat duty. He even renounced his U.S. citizenship at the height of the feverish campaign to encourage renunciations at Tule Lake. But later Yutaka volunteered for the U.S. Army, serving as an interpreter at Schofield Barracks, and regained his citizenship. When he was about to resume a normal life, he was told he had cancer. He died soon after. The carefree days of his youth had been his only happy memories as he had battled pain and a slow death.

The Kageura brothers had not had an easy life, so when Urata played the "childhood days" song, they became nostalgic. Those days, at least, had been free of fear, danger and intimidation. Arm in arm, the school friends had walked down dirt paths, stepping over a stream here, ducking under a tree branch there. The friend-ship they had shared then was even now—after so many years—almost a tangible warmth and strength they could hold close for comfort.

One day, the internees at Honouliuli were told the Empress of Japan had sent, through the Red Cross, some medicine, food and tea. But when the men opened the tub of *miso*, the soy bean paste, it had green mold on it.

"Ugh! It took so long to get here, it's spoiled," the men mourned. But throw away something sent by the Empress?

"You have to sign for this tub of miso, and you had better dispose of it fast," the commander said.

Tetsuo Oi and Dan Nishikawa, two internees in liaison jobs, dis-cussed what they should do. Suddenly Nishikawa jumped to his feet.

"*Aokabi*," he said triumphantly.

"*Aokabi*?"

"Yes. I learned this in science class in Japan. When miso develops aokabi, it is most delicious. This *miso* is not spoiled."

Together the two wiped off the green mold with wet cloth, then scraped about an inch of the miso off the top. This they saved to use in pickling their vegetables. The rest of the miso was usable and delicious. Nishikawa and Oi were the heroes of the day, not only to the internees but to the POWs in the tents beyond the 10' high fence, for they too, were able to drink miso soup and to use the bean paste to flavor their fish and vegetables.

When Dan Toru Nishikawa was first taken from the Sand Island camp to Honouliuli because Sand Island was discontinued as an internee camp beginning March 1, 1943, he was shocked upon seeing the living quarters. The huts had *kiawe* trees growing through holes in the floor. The internees borrowed hammers, nails, saws, picks and scraps of lumber. It took about ten days to repair the barracks to make them habitable. Each hut accommodated eight to twelve men.

A few days later, officials from Fort Shafter came to assess needed repairs and materials. They were surprised and pleased to find the huts had already been repaired and the surrounding area cleaned. The Honouliuli officials were proud of the work they had managed to get done "for free," and received high praise. The men who had actually done the work were not even acknowledged.

"An official took credit for the job and got promoted," an angry Nishikawa said.

Nishikawa was a *kibei*. He had been born in Honolulu on Jan. 2, 1906, but had been taken by his parents to Japan and left with his grandparents for an education. Upon graduating from high school he attended college for a while, but because of immigration law changes, his father recalled him to Hawai'i in 1926. He then attended Mid-Pacific High School to learn English.

After he was picked up, his money in the bank was frozen. His wife's sewing school was closed, and the family had no means of support. She was forced to live with a sister in Wahiawā, O'ahu.

Camp in the early days of the war was disorganized. One midnight, on July 27, 1942, "Sampan" Yoichi Kagimoto, 48, complained of a severe stomachache. His brother took him to the dispensary, where he received a handful of something that looked like Epsom Salt. Cradling his stomach because of severe spasms, "Sampan" attempted to walk or crawl the sandy path to the bathroom, muttering obediently "prisoner...prisoner...prisoner..." to the "Halt!" command but died on the way.

Another night, Seiichi Sugimoto found it difficult to breathe. Nishikawa went to call the doctor, but again there was no doctor. Even the captain was not available, so they took Sugimoto to the dispensary, much as they hated to do this after Kagimoto's experience. But there was no one else to turn to; the man at the dispensary gave Sugimoto an injection and told him to come back the next day. When Sugimoto returned, the orderly gave him two Aspirin and something to stop his diarrhea.

"But I don't have diarrhea," Sugimoto cried out in anguish and pain. "I want a doctor...a real doctor... please..."

Then one night Mr. Miura, a Japanese school teacher, complained of severe stomach pain. The captain said they didn't have an ambulance; Miura would have to wait till daylight.

"OK, but I hold you responsible," Nishikawa told the captain. "This is what happened to Mr. Kagimoto on Sand Island and he died. We intend to have this case investigated. Now we are not as naive as we were then, or so scared."

"Oh well," the Captain said. He loaded Miura into his own jeep and drove him to a hospital in town. The stomach pain was diagnosed as acute appendicitis and Miura had an immediate operation. Within four days Miura was sent back to recuperate at camp.

One day at Honouliuli, as at Mainland camps in various states ranging from North Dakota, Arizona, Idaho, Wyoming, Colorado, Utah and Arkansas, the men were asked, "Are you willing to serve in the armed forces of the United States on combat duty wherever ordered?"

"Hell no," many of them answered. Those who said "no" were labeled disloyal and shipped to Tule Lake in northern California. They included Seiichi Sugimoto, Shigeo Fujino, Shinzaburo Sumida, Noriaki Atsuumi and Rev. Kenjitsu Tsuha.

"Why didn't they enlist us earlier? Before stigmatizing us, shaming us, and making our families so miserable? On Dec. 7, I would have been the first to volunteer, but after so many years, no…"

Many, however, spent sleepless nights wondering whether that decision had been the right one.

Of all the internees, the cooks led the most hectic life. Once, as the men were about to eat dinner, 11 Japanese POWs were brought in, defiantly singing *Aikoku Koshinkyoku*, a song which proclaimed their love of Japan.

"Could you hustle something for them to eat? I don't think they even had lunch," Capt. Spillner asked.

"Sure."

Extra men left their own food and went with the cooks back into the kitchen to prepare an emergency meal, which included rice, miso soup, luncheon meat, vegetables and tea. They left the food on a separate table and returned to their own dinner, which was by then cold and unappetizing.

When they returned to clear the POWs' table, they found the men sitting ramrod straight, with food untouched.

"What's the matter? Food not good enough for you? We can't do much on such short notice," they told the POWs.

"It isn't that. This is enemy food. We don't touch enemy food. And it could be poisoned."

"By us? Poisoned by us? When we're fellow Japanese? And what do you mean…enemy food. Don't you know part of this food was sent to us by your government? This *miso* is from the Empress; this tea was sent by your *Kunai-cho* through the Red Cross. The food was collected from the Japanese people and after much negotiation, sent to internees here and on the Mainland."

"Oh..." they bowed to the food, as if to the Empress of Japan.

"And another thing. You'll be sent to the Mainland U.S. soon. This camp is only a way station, except for us. We're *nisei*, but because we were educated in Japan, we are considered 'possibly dangerous' to the U.S. But you POWs will be exchanged for American POWs in Japan, and when you return to Japan you'll be able to fight for your country once again. So starving here is a wasteful act..." The man who was presumably the leader bowed and commenced eating. The others followed joyfully, and in no time the food was gone.

"*Domo arigato,*" they bowed their thanks and followed a sergeant to their barracks.

Soon after they left for the Mainland came 200 Korean laborers captured from Makin Island, north of Tarawa. They talked endlessly, but no one could understand them. Actually they understood Japanese, for once when one of the Hawai'i men said, in Japanese, "Look, what's that?" the Koreans looked in that direction curiously. But in front of the Japanese, the Koreans spoke their own language.

A group of 30 Koreans decided to pitch their tents in the baseball field.

"Get them out of there...get them out..." The Hawai'i men cried. "We can't play baseball." The captain, the sergeants, the Hawai'i men requested that the group of 30 go back to the tents provided them. Nothing anyone said could persuade them to leave. They pretended they couldn't understand Japanese or sign language.

"Let's beat one of them up," was a suggestion.

"And lose visitation rights? Not worth it," the others said.

Finally the huge group left for the Mainland, much to the relief of the Hawai'i internees.

Then came two more Koreans. They wouldn't eat, and, when

threatened, invited being shot. Finally Sgt. Loveless asked the locals to find out what was troubling them. These Koreans did not pretend they could not speak Japanese.

"There were four of us fighting together on one of the islands in the Pacific," the two Koreans explained. "When we were captured, two were wounded and I think they died. We want to die too. We made a pact we would die together."

Capt. Spillner said, "Oh, so that's it. Listen, tell them the other two are in a hospital."

"Ah so?" But there was skepticism and disbelief on their faces.

"OK, so we'll have to show them."

A sergeant and a guard took the two Koreans to the hospital, some two-story buildings on a ridge at Fort Shafter. When the four were reunited, they squealed in joy.

"Look at this room! Look at this bed! Look at cleanliness! Look at nurse! Look at food!" The two men found everything a novelty. "Americans good. Americans kind. Japan, no good. Japan, no kind. Make Korean go danger place." They had been captured working somewhere in the South Pacific.

When they were returned to the camp, there was nothing they wouldn't do to keep the camp clean and scrubbed. They beamed at and saluted every officer, every private. The Hawai'i Japanese internees hated to see the cheerful two go.

Soon after they left, six healthy Japanese sailors arrived. Each day, they changed their clothes and practiced *sumo*. Nothing distracted them from their practice. They didn't care that Japan had lost a major battle, or that an amateur cook had scorched the rice.

And when they left for the Mainland, they didn't even thank the Japanese internees who had cooked their meals, washed their clothes, and cleaned up after them. They seemed to expect homage, and they left with heads high, almost as dignitaries.

"Lousy wrestlers..." someone muttered.

"Hey, they're not wrestlers, at least the way we think of wrestlers. They're *sumo tori*, and they have something to do with religion. They're been honored in Japan for centuries…"

"But they're still prisoners…"

"Yes, but they're *sumo tori* first and prisoners second. They'll always be *sumo tori* or connected with *sumo* somehow, but they won't always be prisoners. Maybe they were entertainers on the ship, and they don't worry about which country wins or loses. Wars are won or lost, but *sumo* goes on forever."

"*Sumo tori* or wrestlers, I'm glad they're gone. They ate so much of our Japanese food, and left us with bread and chili con carne."

Henry Tokutaro Tanaka on the island of Kaua'i awoke on February 10, 1942, at the usual time and, after breakfast, hurried to his radio appliance shop. It was next to impossible to buy new radios, so the repair business was booming.

When he was abruptly picked up, he was asked, "Have you been to Japan?" From the corner of his eye, Tanaka had seen the dates when he had left for Japan and when he had returned. "Why do they want to play games for?" he thought. "Why not ask me, 'Are you pro-Japan or pro-United States?'"

Although he answered truthfully and he could see no reason why he should be interned, he was taken to Wailua County Jail and placed with ten to fifteen others. For two weeks, no visitors were allowed, so they wore the same clothes until finally one day his wife was allowed to visit him. She brought him clean clothes.

After about three-and-a-half months, he was notified he would be sent to Sand Island on O'ahu, from where he was transferred to Honouliuli when Sand Island Camp was closed.

Back home on Kaua'i, his wife tried to collect the debts owed them for the sale of radios and for repairs done by Henry.

"Get away from my yard or I'll call the cops," some of the customers yelled. "I don't owe any Jap anything!"

"You don't move, I'll sic the dogs on you!"

"You want your damn radio back? Here!" Bang, came a radio thrown full force into the yard. Mrs. Tanaka would weep as she walked the two or three miles back to her home.

Finally, after two years and four months, Tanaka was on the verge of a nervous breakdown and was hospitalized. "Tell me why I'm being held," he insisted. "At least I want to know what my crime is." A few days later, two men came and interrogated him, then said they were paroling him but "You'll have to sign a form stating you will not sue the government in the future," they warned.

Because he was on parole, he had to report to the police station every week and to the military office once a month. There he was asked, "Have you bought government bonds? Have you been out after the 10 p.m. curfew? Have you donated your services to the Kiawe Corps?" The Kiawe Corps helped clear beaches of the trees with the treacherous thorns.

Since he had worked as a communications helper and as a weapons man before being interned, he was asked to work on the island of Guam in the Pacific. Tanaka answered, "I'm on parole. I have to report to the police each week. How can I leave the island?"

"We can arrange that."

"No, I want to stick to the rules of my parole." They had not trusted him earlier. Why should they trust him now on a job of a confidential nature? It gave him some satisfaction to know that his services were needed, but since they had squandered almost three years of his life, why donate more years separated from his ill wife? Why had they not used him earlier? He would have been proud to give his time...his life...to his country!

When Tanaka had attended high school many years ago, his family had been so poor he did not have a pair of shoes to wear to school until his junior year. A Caucasian woman hired him for odd jobs so he could earn money for books. Later, when he became established as a businessman, he remembered her with flowers. Now he learned she was critically ill.

Tanaka went to see her at the hospital, but she refused to see him. "Tell him I'm extremely disappointed in him because he's been disloyal to his country," she said. Tanaka wept. How could she, an intelligent woman and a leader in the community who knew just about everything that happened in that small town judge him disloyal when he himself didn't know what his crime had been? Some uneducated, prejudiced townsmen, yes, but surely not this woman who had known him from age 10, and whom he had respected so highly!

"The trauma of being tainted with the suspicion of disloyalty has left a scar on my heart," he said. "How many other people...even friends...believe I was or am disloyal? And if my country made a mistake about me, why doesn't it acknowledge it publicly so I can be Henry Tanaka, a loyal citizen, again? If it didn't make a mistake...if I've been disloyal...then I'll take my punishment willingly. I'm only one human being, but I am a human being with feelings and should be treated as such, especially by my own country. When people look at me, what are they thinking? When they look away, why? Must my wife and I always carry this burden? A burden we can't throw off because we don't know what it is?"

Dec. 6, 1941 was a big night for Gunichi Takahashi and Kimie Sera of Haleʻiwa. They were getting married that evening and had planned a big party for most of the fishermen in the area and other friends. At that time as many as 281 sampans would leave in the early evening for a night of fishing, returning early the next day. But on Dec. 6, the waters were clear of any sampans. The owners were eating, drinking and singing at the Takahashi wedding.

The sampan owners did not know how lucky they were that Gunichi and Kimie had married that night. Otherwise, they would have been in the ocean on Dec. 7. Two hundred sampans heading for shore at Haleʻiwa, with an air force base only a few miles away, would have been a sure target for planes searching for the Japanese fleet with its carrier-based fighters and dive-bombers.

One of Gunichi Takahashi's best friends was James K. Omizo. Jimmy, as he was affectionately called by the people of Haleʻiwa, owned a small one-man sampan, and he would motor out in the evening to hook *menpachi, aji,* ōpakapaka, kāhala and ulua and net crab, lobster, squid and octopus. What he couldn't sell, he would give to friends and neighbors.

Born on the Big Island in 1906, Jimmy had been taken by his father to Japan when he was six. When he returned to Hawaiʻi in 1920, at age 14, he didn't know any English. To make matters worse, his father died the following year, leaving Jimmy to fend for himself.

The following years were desperate ones for the young man who should have been in school but couldn't afford it. He worked at several jobs, hardly knowing where his next meal would come from. Then he turned to fishing, which became his livelihood. He married a girl who had left school at 13 to care for an ill mother, and who began work at age 15.

When a K. Kanazawa came and told him he was needed for questioning, he was astonished.

"Me? You sure it's me? Give me an American uniform and I'll fight for my country anywhere, any time. You're absolutely sure it's me you're supposed to pick up?"

He asked that they contact a Col. Dinly and a Capt. Frizelle who would vouch for his honesty, integrity and loyalty.

A week after he was taken from the Immigration Office to Sand Island, he was returned to the Immigration Office. He was elated. Col. Dinly and Capt. Frizelle had vouched for him.

To his disappointment he found that he was being interrogated again, and his new interrogators were Masatoshi Katagiri and Hiroshi Fujioka. Katagiri, he had heard, was somehow connected with the FBI, but in what capacity he didn't know, nor had he cared. He only knew people were afraid of Katagiri.

"Why am I being held?" he asked.

"Didn't you spend your early years in Japan? From age 6 to 14? Those are the most formative years in a person's life, you know."

"But I was taken to Japan when I was only a child," he protested. "I lived in Japan eight years, in Hawai'i 22 years...almost three times as long."

"How much English schooling do you have?"

How could Jimmy explain to these college graduates that he had had to work to live. Education was a luxury, when one didn't have parents at age 14. These two who confronted him... surely they had been raised in a family and had had more than a 10¢ plate of stew and rice for supper. How much English school did he have...it was like poking pins under his fingernails. How many times he had stood outside a high school, wondering what it would feel like to spend the day sitting in classrooms with books and friends!

"How can anyone call me disloyal?" he questioned. "Look, ask my wife Jane for letters I received for helping in rescue work of military personnel. How many times I've risked my own life in 20-foot waves, searching for lost military personnel. My sampan would be swamped, but I kept on searching. I'd get calls at any time of the day and night. I even have a letter from Admiral Kimmel. Ask my wife Jane."

Jane did have the letters. One was from the Headquarters, 14th Pursuit Wing, Office of the Commanding General, Wheeler Field, Territory of Hawai'i and signed by H.C. Davidson, Brigadier General, Air Corps, which read:

Dear Mr. Omizo:

I wish to thank you for the splendid work and generous assistance you rendered in the attempt to locate the missing Naval officer who drowned some months ago near Haleʻiwa, and also your rescue work in connection with the wreck of the Army Crash boat. Your unselfish assistance is a source of gratification and I thank you for the help which you so kindly rendered.

Sincerely yours,   October 7, 1941

The letter from Admiral Husband E. Kimmel, Commander-in-Chief of the U.S. Navy's Pacific Fleet went as follows:

Despite his volunteer service, James Omizo was advised that "after careful consideration of your case by the hearing board and reviewing authorities, it appears necessary to intern you for the duration of the war to safeguard the security of the Hawaiian Department."

Safeguard the security of the Hawaiian Department from me? It seemed unbelievable. But Omizo was given the number ISB-HUS-CI 719.

Jane Omizo had been so proud of the letter from Admiral Kimmel when it had first arrived. She had had it framed and hung in her living room. Now, she realized, it hadn't been worth the cost of the frame she had purchased for it.

Was this the American way of life? Jane wrote a letter to Lt. Gen. Robert C. Richardson, Jr., Office of the Military Governor. She said:

My husband is an American citizen, and to the best of my knowledge has always taken pride in this fact. As a fisherman operating out of Waialua Bay, he has always been active in voluntarily working for the Army and Navy, whenever the use of his boat or his services were necessary. An investigation by your office will no doubt convince you that he was the one on whom the Army and Navy always called on for help in searching for and rescuing fliers and sailors.

Before my husband's internment and more so at present, I have been sick and have undergone three major operations. Your offices were once so kind as to have my husband temporarily released for about half a day, at the time of my third major operation. Due to these operations and because of the doctor's orders, I have to this date been unable to resume my work.

We have a son twelve years of age, and our son does most of the housework and cooking and washing to help me. He even goes to work two days a week, which to some extent helps me financially.

There was no answer. There was no acknowledgement that the letter had even reached a person who could make decisions.

Five months later, Jane Omizo met her friend, Andrew Anderson, a Bank of Hawai'i manager.

"Jane, how are you? And how's Jimmy," he asked. "I've been on the Mainland, you know." It was February 11, 1944.

When Anderson heard Jane's cry for help, he said, "Let's see what I can do. I'll go and visit Jimmy tomorrow."

The next day, Jimmy was escorted home!

Admiral Kimmel's letter again hangs on the living room wall. That he was unfairly dishonored by Washington, D.C. made the letter even more poignant. It was not only the Japanese-American who had to be punished because Pearl Harbor had not been prepared for the sneak attack; there had to be a military scapegoat!

COMMANDER-IN-CHIEF
UNITED STATES FLEET

Pearl Harbor, T.H.
April 2, 1941.

Dear Mr. Omizo:

The Commander-in-Chief, Pacific Fleet,
wishes to take this opportunity to express his
thanks and appreciation for the valuable assistance rendered by you on the night of March 21st
in connection with the search for Lieutenant
Leggett at Kawailoa Bay in that you assisted in
operating the two sampans, making it possible to
continue the search for Lieutenant Leggett and
the members of the crash boat crews after the
crash boats had been swamped.

Such acts of courage and cooperation by the
civilian population are well received, and deeply
appreciated by the Services of our country.

Very truly yours

H. E. KIMMEL
Admiral, U. S. Navy
Commander-in-Chief, Pacific Fleet.

Mr. James K. Omizo,
Haleiwa, Oahu.

CHAPTER 18

SANTA FE:

But Integrity Counts Too

"We're being moved to Santa Fe. Isn't that in New Mexico?"

"Yes. New Mexico. That's mostly Indian territory. Well, the camp is bound to be a desert again, if that's where the Indian reservations are."

At the beginning of the war, the Hawai'i internees had not been told to where they were being sent. But now, after two years, officials could explain that smaller camps such as Lordsburg, Livingston, and Missoula were being phased out. Internees would be concentrated at Santa Fe, a Department of Justice enemy alien camp.

On March 20, 1943, 357 men were moved from Livingston to Santa Fe. On April 6, the group which included Masayuki Chikuma, the cook who provided storytelling as well as food, and Kumaji Furuya reported back from Missoula, Montana. Then, was it May 30? a group of men including editor Yasutaro Soga and judo instructor George Hoshida arrived from Lordsburg. Soon after, 216 Peruvians and Bolivians came from Camp Kennedy, Texas. The South Americans brought 900 books plus laughter, youth, and the prospect of baseball games. There were now over 1,600 at Santa Fe.

Santa Fe, they found, was an old city with "Santa" meaning "saint" and "Fe" having to do with religion. It was near the Pueblo Indian Reservation. Towns had Japanese-sounding names like Tesque and Nambe.

About 1540, Spaniard Francisco Coronado had brought 500 soldiers to this area. Then, in 1840, the French came. In 1912, the area was annexed to the United States. Now, in 1943, it was thousands of Japanese. The Indians had seen many races, but the faces that looked most like theirs were the ones behind barbed wire fences, guarded by soldiers with machine guns.

Moving from camp to camp was no longer a chore for the men. It had become routine. The men packed like professional travelers. And once they reached the new camp and were assigned barracks, they elected a barrack leader.

The barrack leaders then elected a block leader—laughingly but lovingly called "block head." This leadership group outlined duties and responsibilities, developed communication lines with camp officials, and worked out problems through outlined procedures as much as possible.

They immediately organized classes, utilizing old and new talent: English, Japanese, Spanish, history, philosophy, geography, woodcarving, painting and drawing, calligraphy, and various forms of Japanese music and dancing.

The field trips were especially exciting. Dr. Kano, the field trip leader, told them this area once had been an ocean. So that was why they found rocks etched with the imprint of fish! Nature had been at work there for millions of years. Now, what were four years in a man's life—to give four or five or maybe even eight years—to the country to which they had emigrated and which had given them and their children a good life? They could have served in many other ways, but if keeping them in camps was the way the government wanted them to serve, then this would be the way they would serve. So the men kept busy, trying to remain physically and mentally alert.

At 2:30 a.m. the morning of June 23, 1943, the dinner bell rang, followed by short blasts of the laundry steam whistle. At these familiar sounds at such an unusual hour, the men hastily donned clothes and rushed outside. "Fire! Fire!" shouts reverberated. The messhall was in flames!

Because the flames were reaching toward the hospital, the library, the recreation room and the tailor shop, the men ran to help. Orderlies were carrying patients to safety. Internees and soldiers alike tried to save whatever could be carried out of the buildings in the path of the fire.

After what seemed hours, a fire truck from Santa Fe reached the camp. By this time the messhall had burned down and the flimsy tarpaper buildings called Barracks 1 and 2 were gutted beyond repair. The exhausted men made room for those who had been burned out and tried to get some sleep.

The next morning, the men prowled in the ruins of the messhall. Curiously, some found eggs with unbroken shells!

"Breakfast will be late this morning. It's being prepared by inmates at the state prison near Santa Fe," the internees were told. They waited patiently. At 8:30, a truck drove up. Each man was rationed to one cup of coffee, one bun, and one boiled egg. Lunch, however, proved more filling, and by evening, federal officials had corraled enough food and arranged for kitchen facilities to feed the 1,600 internees.

In the days that followed, a strange relationship developed between internees and guards. Where they had followed a role of captor and captive in the past, now they demonstrated greater cooperation. After all, had they not voluntarily fought a common enemy—a fire?

Men from all corners of the camp—even the guards from the watchtowers—had scurried to carry patients and equipment out to safety, often entering burning buildings and endangering their own lives. Others had carried precious supplies from the hospital, had pushed and pulled other equipment from other buildings. They had banded together without any orders. Their conscience, in the few seconds after the cry "Fire!" had gone out, had been their guide.

From that fiery crucible, the two sides regarded each other more kindly, and each ignored or minimized minor irritations. Newcomers to the camp did not share this feeling of cooperation, but they could sense the harmony that existed.

But then a group of 70 men came from Tule Lake Center in Northern California. It was strange how only 70 men, placed in separate barracks, could create disharmony among 1,600 men.

The newcomers were young and vigorous. They were up each morning before the sun arose, and exercised loudly, then jogged to the chant of "Wasshoi… wasshoi… wasshoi." As the sun peeped from the horizon, they all got on their knees and bowed reverently to the east, to the "rising sun."

And when the officials told the Tule Lake Gang, as the others called them, to turn in sweatshirts which read "Down with America," the gang members refused. "Imprisoning us is your business. What we wear is our business," they claimed. Ten days later, these shirts were forcibly taken from them.

One day…in fact, it was on a 13th, a bad luck day…the cavalry came and took two of the leaders who were Hawai'i men: Z. Tachibana and K. Tsuha. They were escorted to Upper Town, the newer section of the camp which housed administration, the Germans, and the Italians. Anxious to know why the two were taken in such a fashion, the rest of

211

the Tule Lake Gang followed.

Seeing the crowd of men, the guards, afraid of violence, sprayed tear gas at the Tule Lake Gang with the purpose of dispersing them. Unfortunately, because of the strong wind, the tear gas blew back at them, at which the Gang laughed and jeered. Humiliated and angry, some of the guards hit the Gang members, who, hurt and bloody but more bloody than hurt, were taken to the hospital. This, of course, garnered sympathy for the Gang from camp residents.

Most of the Hawai'i residents, however, did not want violence. "Look at how unfriendly this camp has become since you people came," they complained.

"Unfriendly? So long as life is pleasant, livable, you don't care? Three meals a day, a bed, and heat in winter—and you're satisfied."

"No. We're not satisfied. We're not satisfied, but we can accept the situation in which we've been put. We have to accept this situation for the duration of the war."

"You're spineless. Where's your Japanese character, your *dokyo*? Your strength? Your courage? You're not even concerned about the issue of internment, so long as life is livable. We from the Mainland are concerned about injustice done to us. Is it right for a government to intern its own people? Its own citizens?"

"But why pester the officials and guards here? They're not decision-makers. They just follow orders, like us."

"Precisely! And unless we make noise and get publicity, how do we get the decision-makers in Washington D.C. to notice us and to think about their actions ? If we make a lot of noise in some unusual way, some leaders in Washington are bound to hear us."

"We heard about some of the problems you people in Tule Lake had," the Hawai'i internees said. "It seems strange that you had so many problems, so many confrontations, while we at Livingston, Lordsburg, Missoula, McCoy and here at Santa Fe had so few. We've been treated rather well. We have adequate food, recreational activities, newspapers and magazines, movies, self-rule…what can we complain about?"

"Sure, these officials treat you well. But remember, this is a Department of Justice camp. You're protected by Geneva Convention rules. The Spanish consulate helps you out. On the other hand, most of the Mainlanders are at War Relocation Authority—WRA—camps, and ours are run by the Army. We don't have anyone to whom we can turn. The President? The Constitution? The Supreme Court? Nah, in times of war, the three departments in Washington are all under the Chief Executive—the President—and he's influenced by his Chiefs of Staff."

"I guess you're right. But why do you people speak so harshly, so stridently, as if you were Japan Army officers yourselves? Why, some of you are priests. I thought priests were peace-loving people?"

"We are! We are! We're peace loving, but we love integrity more, we love honor. We won't sacrifice our integrity just because we're treated well or we want to be treated well. It's the principle of the thing. How can the Americans—the Army—Washington—say we're criminals who must be locked up in camps? When they haven't proven we did anything wrong? When they only "fear" we might do something, they "are afraid" of us or "suspect" us? Are we to live all our lives with the label of "criminal" or "prisoner" or "parolee" when our whole lives have been dedicated to mankind? Perhaps those of us who have been trained as priests see life—which is so transient—differently from you. We don't mean we're better than you. We just mean we have different values. A single life…especially our own…is not the most precious thing on earth. We die, but some things…like integrity, like honor…live forever, if people fight to keep them. Give up a little integrity, and the next time you give up more. Then our younger people, the next generation, will grow up with less and less integrity. Is that the kind of nation we want for our children and grandchildren?"

"I understand…No, how could I understand when I don't have to give up my home, my business, my community? How can I understand fully the depth of your pain, your anger, your *nasakenasa*? I can understand only with my mind, not my soul…"

Soon another contingent of angry Tule Lakers came to Santa Fe. But this time, instead of isolating all the newcomers into their own barracks, the officials placed two Tule Lakers into each barrack of Hawai'i and Peru internees.

"So the officials believe we can influence the two Tule Lakers. What if they influence us instead? That would be a big joke."

Beside the Tule Lakers, there were some elderly Stateside internees who arrived from Bismarck, North Dakota. These *issei* from the West Coast also differed from Hawai'i's *issei* in their perspective of internment and camp life.

For example, there was the matter of apple picking!

Last year, Furuya had gone apple picking at Missoula, Montana. He remembered the first juicy bite into a Yakima apple picked from a tree…so different from the crumbly fruit sold in Hawai'i. He remembered the joy with which those left behind ate the apples which those who went brought back in their trousers, tightened at the bottom with leggings. They had stuffed their shirt sleeves, their shirts, and even their hats with apples. Then they had walked like Zombies, like robots, to the truck. That had been such a fun time! The only decision they had to make then was whether they were strong and healthy enough to endure a day of picking apples and climbing up and down a stepladder. After all, so few of them were accustomed to manual labor.

Here, at Santa Fe, there were orchards across the river, at a place called Tesque. Even the name was intriguing, sounding like the Japanese "to save."

The apple orchard owners asked the Army if the internees could be used as apple pickers for $3 a day. That meant pickers would be able to earn in six days more than what they earned in a month at camp. Besides, there would be those crisp, juicy fruit!

But now, with the Bismarck, North Dakota Mainlanders with

them, the decision to go or not to go was not that simple.

"Listen, when we were chased out of California, New Mexico residents wouldn't allow Japanese on their farms. They were afraid we might settle here. The governor and mayors voted not to allow any Japanese in this state. 'If the Japs want jobs during the duration of the war, tell them to go to Chicago or New York, or better yet, send them all to Japan. We definitely don't want Japs here.' And now, do you want to save their crop? Just because they can't find enough Mexicans to do the job?"

"But the apples will spoil..."

"Good! Let them spoil. Those growers need us now. Is it to your advantage to go, or to theirs?"

"We could both benefit..."

"Listen, those big growers, they don't even live in this area. They're not small farmers. Small farmers pick their own fruit. Big growers live in huge mansions near cities. They pay starvation wages to the Mexicans; the Indians won't even work for them. Do you think they have any consideration for you...or for the Mexicans or the Indians?"

"It seems such a crime to let those delicious apples go to waste..."

"Ask yourself, Furuya. Ask the men in your barracks, in the other barracks. Are you helping 'good' people, 'deserving' people? If the answer is 'yes,' then go."

In the end, Furuya decided not to go. Out of close to two thousand men, only twenty or so finally went because they needed the money desperately. The growers were forced to pay the Mexicans more than they had intended.

How naive we were in Missoula, Montana, when the call for apple pickers came, Furuya and the others reminisced. The Montana farmers wanted apple pickers; we picked apples. The apple growers told the town people what hard workers we were and how we had saved their crop; the town people appreciated that and welcomed us when we were allowed to go into town. The camp officials were good to us because the town people commended them. The commander allowed us to plan and carry out more recreational activities. A chain of good seemed to follow our naive apple picking. We didn't even realize we were helping the enemy.

"Yes," Ozaki agreed. "We didn't even know the governor of Montana too had refused to allow Japanese to resettle in Montana. All we knew was that without us the apple crop would be ruined." He paused. "You know, maybe next time...maybe...if there ever is a next time...the mayor of Missoula will speak up and insist, 'Let's accept the Japs in Montana. They're hard workers. When we needed them badly, they put their bitterness aside and helped us.'"

Would there ever be such brave men? Would their voices be heard? In a new time and place?

The West Coast internees and the Hawai'i internees were both entitled to their way of looking at situations, the Hawai'i men acknowledged. And how much more sophisticated the West Coast young men were, in comparison with the elderly islanders. Even the names of governing committees showed this.

At Tule Lake Center the committees were called Executive Committee, Organization and Planning, Relocation, Leave Clearance, Finance, Ordinance, Education, Transportation and others.

The Hawai'i committees were News, Farming, Health, Store, Laundry, Education, Police, Entertainment, Food, Recreation, Shoes, Liquor, Movies, Hospital, Chicken and Barber Committees.

The men sighed. "Chicken Committee! Liquor Committee! Barber Committee! Shoes Committee! Looks like we're concerned only with our stomachs and looks!"

But they didn't change the names of their committees. They said the titles were very clear to young and old. Why shouldn't life be simple?

Nizo Nishizaki died July 24, 1943 while at Santa Fe Camp. Attending his funeral was his son Ogden Masaichi, who was serving in the U.S. Army at that time.

Photo Courtesy Irene Kanno

CHAPTER 19

TULE LAKE:

Now, What Was the Crime?

Tule Lake Center, according to those who came from that camp, was a hellhole. One wouldn't know what a concentration camp was unless he had been there.

Two questionnaires influenced the composition of Tule Lake internees and their emotions.

The first questionnaire was the "Statement of United States Citizenship of Japanese Ancestry (Selective Service Form 304A)." As written, circulated and administered to all *nisei* over age 17, the questionnaire included questions No. 27 and No. 28.

No. 27 asked:

Are you willing to serve in the armed forces of the United States on combat duty wherever ordered?

Unlike Hawai'i, where most of the families of internees continued to live in their own homes and had resumed a more-or-less normal life, the West Coast men had no anchor to their lives. If they went into the armed forces, what would happen to their parents, their grandparents? their younger brothers and sisters? Even those from Hawai'i often felt compelled to say, "No, unless...unless my wife and child are sent back to Hawai'i...or...unless my brother is left behind to care for my aged parents..." But "unless" conditions were ignored. If the answer was "no" then the individual was dubbed disloyal.

The questionnaire was renamed "Application for Leave Clearance" and was administered to all *issei*—alien male and female 17 years or older. This time Question #27 had been revised to:

> If the opportunity presents itself and you are found qualified, would you be willing to volunteer for the Army Nurse Corps or the WAAC?

Many of the *issei* men and women who had spent a lifetime farming under the hot California sun and who were now in their 60s to their 80s could have answered "Yes" knowing they would never be called, but being honest, they answered "No."

Question 28 created even more confusion because it was a two-part question. It read:

> Will you swear unqualified allegiance to the United States of America and faithfully defend the United States from any or all attack of foreign or domestic forces, and forswear any form of allegience or obedience to the Japanese emperor, to any other foreign government, power or organization?

Yes, they would swear allegiance to the United States of America, but how could they forswear any form of allegiance to the Japanese government when that was the only country which provided them citizenship? If they answered "yes" to this question, and they were repatriated or deported to Japan during or after the war, would Japan have a legal obligation to accept them? If not, where could they go? Would they not be "men without a country"?

The answer to the first part of the question would be "yes" but the second part would have to be "no."

When the confusion created by Question 28 was reported to those who had designed the questionnaire, a revision was made, to read:

> Will you swear to abide by the laws of the United
> States and to take no action which would in any way
> interfere with the war effort of the United States?

The answer to that question was an emphatic "yes." But the questionnaires had already been filled and collected. The "no-no" groups, chiefly *kibei*, were sent from different camps in the different states to Tule Lake, which was then designated as the camp for the "disloyals."

After this interchange of internees among the centers, Tule Lake had 6,000 "no-no" individuals remaining from its original 18,000 or about 33 per cent of the total. The incoming "no-no" internees from all the other camps totaled 10,000. The new 16,000 Tule Lakers were angry and vociferous, as compared to other WRA and Department of Justice camps.

The second questionnaire that brought great heartache and split families was Public Law 504, signed by the 78th Congress into law on July 1, 1944. PL 504 was perhaps more cruel than Executive Order 9066, which had provided for mass removal of Japanese from the West Coast, for PL 504 was an instrument which provided for renunciation of American citizenship when the internees were bombarded with hysteria and hostility both from within and from outside the camp.

Within their own camps, there was the fear of bodily harm from the pro-Japan group advocating renunciation. On the outside there was the fear not only of bodily harm, but of unacceptance of whole families for generations to come. There might be no homes, no jobs, no educational facilities. Perhaps the greatest fear was fear of separation—separation of husband from wife, parents from children, grandparents from the rest. By renouncing their citizenship, they were promised passage to Japan as a family, and surely, once in that country, they would be able to regain their dignity and identity, no matter how poor they were or how battle-scarred the country was. They had faith in Japan; they had lost faith in America's integrity!

Tule Lake, near Oregon and Nevada, had really been a lake at one time. Now it contained both fertile and lava land in its 30,000 acres. The "colonists," as administrators called the internees, occupied a small portion of that acreage. There were the usual barbed wire fences, watch-towers, trained dogs, and machine guns.

As "colonists," the forcibly relocated men, originally from Washington and Oregon Assembly centers, went out each morning to raise vegetables on a 2,900-acre area of land. Like prisoners in model programs, they were checked off as they left the compound and checked in as they returned, tired and dirty. Immediately within the main gate was the Provost Marshal's office, where they and other incoming and outgoing traffic were examined.

Within Tule Lake were 74 blocks, with each block containing 200-250 individuals. Each block had a block manager. Then every eight or nine blocks constituted a ward, and there was a ward manager for about 2,000 individuals each. These elected officials—block managers and ward chairmen—met every Wednesday from 9 a.m. to discuss problems and concerns, and to convey information both ways—up and down.

In February, 1943, when army representatives appeared to recruit volunteers for a combat team to be comprised solely of Japanese young men, many were angry and refused to volunteer under those circumstances. "The Army wants a suicide team. They label us 'disloyal' and now they want to use us as bait."

Where the Mainland quota for recruits had been 3,000, only about 1,200 signed up. In the Hawaiian islands, the quota had been 1,500 but close to 10,000 volunteered.

During this period of turmoil, a farm accident occurred in which an internee was killed and several others injured. Accidents could happen, the internees acknowledged, especially with a young, inexperienced driver. But what infuriated them was that Administration offered the widow only $12 a month compensation. So that was the value of a Japanese! A group organized itself and called itself the *Daihyo Sha Kai*; it urged residents not to return to work on the farm unless certain conditions were met. The conditions included, one, a request for a written apology for the death of the internee. Second, the request was that the "colonists" not be compelled to raise vegetables on such a mass basis. At the time, Tule Lake produce was feeding not only Tule Lakers but the other camps and the Army and Navy as well. "The Army is using us as full-time farmers for $18 a month," the *Daihyo Sha Kai* stated. "Outsiders doing the same work are paid much more and do not have to live in regimented, repressive camps."

On Nov. 1, 1943, the national WRA director Dillon S. Myer visited Tule Lake. The *Daihyo Sha Kai* organized a demonstration in which 2,000 to 5,000 internees were involved. The demonstration had been organized chiefly to let Dillon Myer know that the complaints presented were agreed upon by a majority of the camp internees.

Dillon Myer was said to have acquiesced verbally to most of the demands, and when he left, the crowd gathered around the Administration building had bowed in respect and appreciation. However, a newspaper article in a metropolitan paper claimed that 5,000 men had surrounded the Administration Building with knives and had threatened Dillon Myer. The paper demanded that the Army not cave in to Jap prisoner demands.

Because of the article and its insinuations, Dillon Myer was required to sift through the demands more carefully.

Only two days later, on Nov. 3, 1943, another incident occurred. A non-internee driver was caught in an attempt to take food supplies out of the warehouse at night. The internees had suspected that something of this nature was being carried out, since they saw certain types of food being delivered to the warehouse, but these were never served. The food, they realized, was being appropriated for some other purpose.

Tule Lake was divided into four sections: the administration section, the barracks, the messhall area, and the warehouse and factory. Suspicious, the internees had kept watch on the warehouse area, and a system had been devised to alert the others should an unexpected occurrence take place. When the call for assistance in catching the unauthorized driver and his accomplice came, the men quickly and quietly surrounded the warehouse area. One night watchman and three internees were injured and hospitalized. But the thieves had been caught in the act, and a wrong would be made right.

The next day, Nov. 4, to the amazement and astonishment of the internees, the camp was taken over by the Army, presumably at the request of WRA officials. Armored cars with machine guns thundered in, and tear gas was used to disperse the bewildered crowd gathered in the firebreaks between the different wards. The internees had expected a trial of the driver and watchman for suspicion of theft of food; the loaded truck in the middle of night was evidence. Now here was the Army, threatening them with insubordination and vigilantism! When members of the *Daihyo Sha Kai* demanded justice and publicity of the event, they were detained in the Army Stockade. Others, elected to replace former officers, were in turn detained, until stockade detainees numbered 300!

Even worse, curfew and martial law were put into effect. The Army searched all the apartments of the internees, investigating for and confiscating articles such as hardware, cutlery, radios and foodstuff from which sake could be made, such as rice. Rice, of course, was the Japanese staple.

The Army would not recognize the *Daihyo Sha Kai* as an official body, saying they were not an elected body. And when the Spanish Consul, asked by the internees for assistance, also did not recognize the *Daihyo Sha Kai*, the organization began to crumble. But it soon resurfaced when PL405, the renunciation form, was introduced into the camp.

By Dec. 23, 117 *kibei* had asked for renunciation, and their requests were approved. Seventy of the Japanese-American citizens, now listed as enemy aliens, were sent to Santa Fe. But by the time they left, they had succeeded in encouraging 2,000 others at Tule Lake to seek renunciation; they had even held classes on how to answer questions for renunciation.

On Jan. 26, 1945, and then on February 11, March 4, and March 16, a total of 1016 citizens were turned into "instant aliens" and sent to Santa Fe, New Mexico or Bismarck, North Dakota. Often, they had a one-day notice which informed them that they were no longer citizens of the United States and which stated that they were being sent to another camp on the following day. Their goods had to be packed within that 24-hour period.

Because of the composition and emotions of Tule Lake internees, it had 5,461 renunciants, whereas in the other nine WRA camps, there was a total of only 128 renunciants. By February, 1946, almost 5,000 from Tule Lake were removed to Japan, including 1767 American citizens. All except 49 were minors accompanying parents because they were too young to survive by themselves in the United States, their home.

Despite the many injustices encountered in Tule Lake, there were many who worked hard to maintain order, especially for the children who needed a well-rounded curriculum as well as activities to teach them discipline and order. For example, Rev. Kyojo Naito, Assistant Central Block Manager in the Block Managers' Organization worked to organize and maintain some semblence of a system so that activities could be carried on.

Your duties in such capacity have not always been a pleasant one; on most occasions I know it was just the reverse. However, you stood by the course that you felt was right and by doing so, you can look back on these many events with a great feeling of satisfaction of knowing that you did what you felt in your heart was right.

It must be with feeling of satisfaction to you as I know it is with me, that when you look back on the trying and troublesome times that we have had in this center, that you, as well as other members of the Block Managers' Organization, always worked for a sensible and peaceful solution to all problems; and that because of your work in this organization the residents of this center were able to live a more peaceful life than would have been possible otherwise.

...my hope is that never again in your life will you be faced with the problems that have been faced with here.

So wrote Joe J. Thomas, Administrative Office, WRA Tule Lake Center, to Naito on November 21, 1945, as the internees prepared to leave for home.

When Rev. Gyokuei Matsuura from the island of Hawai'i was transferred to Tule Lake, he became part of the official rice cookers team. He had to wash half a bag of rice—50 pounds—each day and cook the most important part of the meal for 300 people.

Then when the *Chuo Nippon Kyoiku Kai*, the Central Japanese Language Association, was organized and eight schools were established, Rev. Matsuura taught calligraphy and morals (*shushin*) to the students. He was so busy, morning to night, that when he heard the pro-Japan men march and yell *Banzai! Banzai!*, and the guards echo "Bang-bang, Bang-bang" as they shot their rifles into the air, he thought, "How childish they all are." Even when Rev. K. Tsuha, one of the leaders of the *Hōkoku-Dan* "pressure boys" invited him to exercise with them, he answered, "If you will join me in *zazen*—meditation— for one hour, I will exercise with you."

On October 10, 1945, with the war over, Matsuura closed his school and prepared to leave Tule Lake. By December, 1945, he was in Los Angeles, ready to return to Hawai'i on the ship *Shawnee*. He had a daughter Phoebe, born at the beginning of the war, and a son born in Tule Lake at the end of the war. Those had been trying years, but his horizon had been widened, and instead of bitterness he had appreciation for the opportunity to experience different and often difficult situations. He had been an active member of his community behind barbed wire, and because of that, the days had flown by.

Attending Matsuura's school had been little Joyce Michihara, 7, and Robert Michihara, 13. Joyce loved school—both English and Japanese—but Robert preferred fishing in the creek close by.

Their father Iwao had been born in Waimānalo, O'ahu, in 1903. Because there were no schools in the vicinity, Iwao had been sent back to Japan for an education. He returned to Hawai'i in 1917, after having received eight years of formal education.

In October, 1942, Iwao was picked up by Army Intelligence. MPs ransacked his home, where he lived with his wife and five children.

"Are you looking for something special?" the oldest daughter Helen asked innocently. "Maybe I can find it for you."

The MPs ignored her but stopped their search.

After the father's internment, the family was shipped to Jerome, Arkansas, in mid-winter. They reached the recently completed, flimsy barracks on February 11, 1943. There was a coal burner in the middle of their one room, and the five children and mother huddled miserably near the stove.

Eventually Iwao was reunited with his family, but then came the questionnaire with questions #27 and #28. Iwao was an American citizen and could serve in combat duty, but he had five children, spoke little English, and was 40 years old. "No," he answered to question #27, and "no" to question #28. He was categorized as disloyal.

"I want to remain as a family. If I have to be sent to Japan, I want to go with my family."

It was a bitterly cold Christmas Day, 1945, when love and good cheer was supposed to be in the air, that the family that tried to remain together was separated. Daughter Helen chose to return to Hawai'i. Masaharu, who had turned 18, left for Chicago to search for a job. Iwao, his wife, and three younger children were to return to Japan. The parents did not know whether they would ever see their two older children again, separated by so many thousands of miles.

Iwao and his family landed at Yokosuka, then took a train to Hiroshima, where Iwao had gone to school so many years ago. Now it was devastated beyond imagination. Carrying their worldly possessions with them, they walked for a few hours until they reached Yagi, a suburb of Hiroshima. Yagi had been spared the horror of the atom bomb itself, but it nursed the victims, many disfigured and maimed. There was hardly a family that had not lost or was not losing a relative, friend or neighbor who had been near Hiroshima that unbelievable day.

Japan could be considered home to Iwao since he had lived there as a youngster but it was not home to his children. They yearned for their home in Hawai'i, and each one searched for and applied to different sources. It was a long, slow process but finally Robert, who had been 13 when sent to the internment camp, was allowed to return to Hawai'i. He was 22. Henry, then 15, was 30 and Joyce, then 7, was 23 when they returned. Somewhere, somehow, they had missed their years of supposedly joyful youth. They had been plucked from their home, shipped like baggage to the sometimes freezing, sometimes burning hot barracks in Arkansas. Then they had been deported to a city where the dead and dying surrounded them physically and spiritually.

And throughout all those years, when the family was together and also when the family was scattered across thousands of miles of ocean, they asked themselves, "Why were we interned? Was it because father was educated for eight years in Japan?"

They were never told why. They never found out why.

CHAPTER 20

MAN WITHOUT A COUNTRY:

Alien in His Native Land

Among all the internees from Hawai'i, perhaps the most active, the loudest, the angriest young man was Rev. Kenjitsu Tsuha. He had been shipped out of Hawai'i with the first contingent on February 20, 1942 to Camp McCoy, and had been with the members of that group until Livingston, Louisiana, when he and a few others were returned to Hawai'i because they were American citizens. And now here he was at Santa Fe!

"Tsuha, Santa Fe is a camp for enemy aliens, like us. You're a citizen. What are you doing here?" Furuya and the others wanted to know.

"It's a long story," Tsuha said. "Let me begin from the beginning so you can understand why I did what I did. Maybe it's not for me, for you, or even for this generation to judge what I and some thousands of others did. Sometimes I think I did the right thing. Sometimes I think otherwise."

"Why, what did you do? Don't keep us in suspense, Tsuha."

"Wait. As I said, let me start from the beginning, although it may be long and boring. I was only three when my mother died." He held up his hand, to silence someone about to protest. "She and my father, from Okinawa, had been told Hawai'i was a land where they would finally have enough to eat, and rice instead of sweet potatoes. So they emigrated to Hawai'i. But my mother had to work so hard, even after childbirth, that she died when I was three.

"My father took me to Okinawa so my grandmother could raise me. What else could he do? Ask other women to care for me? He tried, he told me later. But the women in those days went to work in the cane fields too, even with children, the way my mother had done. Could my father keep me locked up in the house from 5 a.m. to 6 p.m. ? He even tried that, once, in desperation. My food he left on a chair, because I was too little at three, to reach the top of the table. He told me when he returned, the food was untouched, and I was lying on the floor, shivering and hiccupping from crying all day, and with my hand in my mouth. So what else could he do? He borrowed some money from his friends and took me back to Okinawa to live with his mother.

"Of course at age three I quickly forgot what English and Hawaiian words I knew. But always, while attending elementary and junior-senior high school, I never forgot that I was an American as well as a Japanese. I could not wait to return to Hawai'i. America was my dream, my goal, my vision.

"I was 17, in 1933, when I was finally able to return to Hawai'i. I was shocked to see the number of people without jobs, without adequate food, even, for this was after the Great Depression. Why, this was not a land of opportunity, this was a land of desperation, of helpless, hungry, jobless people. What a blow that was for me to absorb, after all my dreams of America.

"I was able to get a position as a teacher at a Japanese school. My wages were very low, so I got another job assisting as a priest in the communities of ʻEwa and Waipahu.

"Imagine my surprise when the FBI picked me up. Me, a nobody! And, at 26, placed with elderly bishops, corporation presidents, bank managers, community leaders—all of whom I had only read about. I was rather flattered. But why was I picked up? Because I was a Japanese school teacher and priest? But how could any American intelligent and powerful enough to be in a decision-making position believe that all those in these professions were disloyal? And especially me...I was the most loyal American one could hope for. Being an American had been the one thing that had sustained me while living in Japan those fourteen years!

"You remember I was sent with you from the Immigration Station to Sand Island to Angel Park to Camp McCoy to Camp Forrest to Livingston. During all that time—shunted from one place to another—I never challenged a rule or regulation, no matter how silly or ridiculous I thought it was. Remember when you people were saying 'Poisoner' to the guards when going to the latrine at Sand Island at night?"

"Or 'pissoner'?"

"Yes, you were all having a big laugh. Of course I knew you were laughing because you didn't want to cry. But never once did I play such a game. I always properly called out 'Prisoner.' I never once made trouble. Even Eifler liked me."

"And he didn't like just anyone..."

"You remember at Livingston, 19 of us were shipped back to Hawaiʻi. Noriaki Atsuumi, Shinzaburo Sumida, Dr. Kazuo Miyamoto, Rev. Shigeo Fujino and the others? We were being returned to Hawaiʻi because we were American citizens, we were told. At last! Being a citizen meant something. The American Civil Liberties Union—the ACLU—had been fighting for us. We had friends back home!

"Several months after we were returned to the camp at Sand Island, we were given a choice: be interned at Honouliuli Camp near Waipahu, or be relocated to some Mainland WRA camp. From a WRA camp we could leave to work in some Midwestern or Eastern city. I chose the WRA camp to vegetating in Honouliuli.

"But I should have known there were no jobs for a Japanese language school teacher or a Buddhist priest. I could be a dishwasher or janitor if I behaved myself, accepted insults, worked harder and longer than the others, and was satisfied with minimum wages. I didn't mind, but even those jobs were hard to come by for us 'Japs.'"

"You were such a quiet and serious person. How and when did you change?"

"I think my problems really began when the Army asked me, one, if I would be loyal to the United States, and two, if I would serve on combat duty in the armed forces. It was easy to say yes to the first question—to say you'll be loyal—because that's on an idea level. Anyone can swear to be loyal to the United States. After all, it's easier to be loyal than disloyal.

"But to say yes as to whether I would serve on combat duty, that was another matter. As a Buddhist priest, I could not, I cannot accept the idea of killing others. One human being should not be forced to do this to another human being. It doesn't matter whether the other is Japanese, Russian, French, Indian or African. I had returned to Hawai'i when I was 17 to escape being conscripted into the Japanese Army. I did not want to kill for any country."

"But Tsuha, why do you make a nuisance of yourself? Don't you know people say you're militaristic, you're a trouble maker?"

"Ah, but I wasn't like this before, was I? At the camps, I saw babies malnourished because there was a lack of milk. With babies, even a week's food is important. I saw children growing aimlessly, with no guidance, equipment and activities to keep them developing physically, socially and psychologically. As a teacher and priest, I could see these lacks keenly. Then it was difficult to get medical attention for adults, and the ill died when they didn't really need to. But what pained me most were the elderly men and women, people my grandmother's age. They were so tiny and bent over from working on vegetable farms and grape fields for half a century. But every rule, every order, they obeyed quietly. They looked resigned. Had life been dealing them blows like this all their lives, so that another one like internment behind barbed wire was yet another order to be endured passively?

"I asked questions from the officials...politely, at first...and was soon dubbed a trouble maker, especially because of my booming priest and teacher voice. And any time there was any hint of trouble at camp, I was the first to be investigated. You know, I began to understand how prison parolees must feel. After any crime is committed they are the first to be suspected. The camp officials were always watching me and of course that irritated me.

"I exercised in the morning with some others—calisthenics—to keep physically fit. The camp leaders called this military training. When did exercising become military training? In school in Japan we all exercised together, both boys and girls, before entering the classrooms for our studies. Such exercising relaxed us and separated outside activities from school work. We could concentrate better."

"But Tsuha," Furuya asked, "didn't you wear headbands with the Rising Sun painted on it? And T-shirts with 'Down with America' printed on it? What was that for? You knew that would make the officials angry."

Tsuha laughed. "That was to get them to notice us and to at least consider our requests. If you're one of 16,000 to 18,000 meek Japanese, it's pretty difficult to get noticed or have our questions answered. As it is, the officials classified us as troublemakers, but they listened when we spoke. Of course they would do the opposite of what we asked, but knowing that, we would ask the opposite of what we really wanted. When the officials found out we did that, it became a game of wits."

"So you were in a position to demand things, Tsuha?"

"Demand? How could we demand things? 'Demand' requires teeth and power to enforce or back up that demand. We had no power, no strength. We could only make nuisances of ourselves and thus get attention."

"And yet," he added soberly, "I realized more and more that only in the U.S. could I do the things I did and say the things I said and still be protected. Even as I was protesting and demanding that I be sent to Japan as a Japanese citizen, still this nation protected most of my rights. I realized then I had been right in treasuring my American citizenship while I was studying in Japan, when I was a child. I wanted my child— my children—to have this same citizenship. At that point in my life, I had nothing to give to my son except this precious citizenship."

"Why didn't you admit this to the officials? Why did you continue protesting?"

"If only you knew what really went on at Tule Lake! You don't know about rapes, and about lack of medical care, concern, or compassion for those dying of cancer, hepatitis and other illnesses. It will take years, maybe even centuries, before the truth is recorded, if ever. Maybe it's better not to know, for wars bring out the worst among men.   They do things they would never dream of doing in their home town."

"But Tsuha, we were interned too, you know...for as long as you've been interned..."

"Interned in a camp such as Santa Fe? Livingston? Lordsburg? You people play baseball and golf and *go* and you eat well. You can't possibly imagine what it was like at the Tule Lake Stockade and at Leupp, Arizona and Moab, Utah. You would have to experience the heat yourself, locked in without water in an area where even insects and plants could not survive. We weren't cut open and operated on, but we were dried into shells of ourselves. Fortunately a high officer came to examine the stockades and ordered them closed. He at least could see what was happening to us."

"Why didn't you ask for help from the Spanish Embassy?"

"We did. We asked the Spanish Consul to cable Foreign Minister Shigemitsu in Japan for help but we didn't hear anything..."

Tsuha didn't know then that with the report of the Tule Lake investigations the Japan government decided to cut off all exchange of prisoners. The 5,000 captured American soldiers and other prisoners in Japan were to suffer for the mistreatment endured at Tule Lake.

"This is when maybe I made a mistake, Furuya. When the renunciation forms were pushed on us, I was so disillusioned with America that I signed one. After all those years of dreaming in Okinawa and reminding myself that I was an American—*ganbare, ganbare* I had told myself again and again. Yet I signed one of those forms."

With the birth of a son, Tsuha requested that he be permitted to cancel his renunciation. He wanted to remain an American citizen. Others had asked to do so and their requests have been approved.

"For someone like you? Never!" spat an Army officer.

But another officer...a Captain Paul R. Robertson...who had replaced Director Best at Leuppe, spoke quietly with Tsuha. "Don't return to Japan if you don't want to, Tsuha. You can remain in the United States. No one can insist on your leaving. You were born here. Times will change. Wounds will heal. Be patient. Don't nurture hatred, Tsuha. Forgive...forget..."

Forgive? OK. Forget? Never! "Furuya-san, Soga-san, you are older men. You have had many experiences throughout the years. Will we be able to forget, as time goes by, what happened to us? When I was stockaded in that camp at Leupp, I asked myself again and again, 'Why are you interned? Look at all the other Japanese in Hawai'i that weren't. What did I do that they didn't?' The only answer could be, 'Because you were educated in Japan and you are a school teacher and priest.' But was I to be blamed or penalized for having been educated in Japan? Was that a crime I had committed? No! I was only three years old then. The decision to go was not mine. It was my father who had committed a crime by taking a three-year-old to a land where the language was strange, and to live with a woman the child had never seen before. Grandma told me later that I cried for over six months, calling and searching for my father each time we went to the village or to town. I would gaze into each face, to see if I could find my father once again. I thought he had been lost, in this strange place with a strange language and strange people. Yes...it was my father's crime, not mine, for taking me to a foreign land for an education which now branded me disloyal and a zero-class citizen.

"But no, it wasn't my father's fault, either. It was my mother's fault, for dying so early and leaving my father with a small child. How could father work and still care for a child? Every Japanese man, woman and child over 10 worked on the plantation those days—full-time, part-time, or over-time. So it was really my mother's crime, for creating the situation she did. It was my mother the FBI should have picked up, not me, the victim of the crime."

He sighed. "In such stupid ways, Furuya-san, I passed the time at Leuppe Stockade. A thousand times, a million times, I whispered to myself, '*Ganbare*, Tsuha, *ganbare*. Be strong. Hang on.' But to the youngsters, the 18- and 19-year-olds who had been locked up with me at Leuppe, I thundered, 'What are you so tearful about? Are you going to give up so easily? Get up! Get up and act like men!' But inside I was a child myself, fearful, hurt, wondering why my life had turned out this way.

"One day a high official came to inspect us and the camp. He didn't want any pampering of scum like us, the guards told us. But when the official reached our barracks, a heat wave, almost as strong and as visible as an ocean wave, hit him. I was still standing, but some of the boys were lying on the cement floor, unable to stand, almost unable to breathe in the stifling heat.

"The stockade commandant shouted, 'Get up!' The boys tried but they couldn't. It was like they were boneless, a mass of meat slowly drying in that desert air.

The high official returned to the air-cooled office, but beginning that day we were permitted all the water we needed to keep our bodies from dehydrating.

"A week or so later, we were returned to Tule Lake and they closed the Leuppe camp. When we returned, almost all of us from Leuppe and about a thousand others signed our renunciation papers."

From Santa Fe, although most of the Hawai'i internees had been sent home in the winter of 1945, Tsuha was to make a criss-cross journey across the country as he dutifully traveled to Stanton, Texas to San Pedro, California to Crystal City, Texas and finally to Seabrook Farms, New Jersey. No one seemed to know what to do with him and a handful of other renunciants.

"If they don't want to return my citizenship, why don't they send me to my grandmother's home in Okinawa?" he once asked a friendly commander.

"You can't be sent to Okinawa," was the answer. "That's part of the U.S. now."

"Part of the U.S.? Okinawa? You're wrong. Okinawa belongs to Japan. I should know. I lived there for many years."

"Not anymore. Now we call it the Ryukyus, and it belongs to the U.S."

"How can that be? And what about the people? Were they consulted? Was it their choice? Was it my grandmother's choice? I can't believe that."

"Listen, Tsuha, war is war, and the defeated country must accept the conditions of the winner. Japan forfeited the Ryukyus. We need bases there."

"Winner! Sure Japan was defeated. But why? Not after fighting man to man. Because the U.S. dropped two atom bombs. Any nation...not only Japan...would surrender under those circumstances. It would be the only humane thing to do.

"But winner? Do you think America really won? Now what will happen to this world of ours? Sure, America shortened the war and saved many lives, but how many lives may be sacrificed in the future if other nations learn how to make an atom bomb? What if our future wars use atom bombs to begin with, instead of ending them? Why didn't America think before making or dropping such a cruel and indiscriminating bomb that kills anything and everything it can reach?"

"Tsuha, that's not a question for you or for me...you know that."

"I know...I know...I'm sorry. It wasn't your fault the U.S. dropped the bomb and it wasn't my fault Japan's military leaders invaded China and Southeast Asia. But we, the ordinary people, we have to share in some of the blame, maybe, because we didn't protest. Oh, I protested at Tule Lake, but it was too late and for the wrong reason. I and others should have protested against Japan in 1933 and 1934 and on to 1941. Some day some Americans will protest the building and dropping of the atom bomb, but it'll be too late for that too. Other nations may learn how to make an atom bomb and then the countries will start threatening each other."

"That would mean the end of this earth as we know it, Tsuha."

"No. The U.S. dropped it twice already, so what's a couple or a dozen or even a hundred times more? We can get used to any cruelty, I've learned within the past three years. Man learns to endure. He will continue to exist if only he can ganbaru...hang on!"

"What a morbid, pessimistic, frightening stance! Don't worry, Tsuha, the U.S. is the only nation capable of making an atom bomb, and while that's true, we'll be safe from aggression. No other nation will dare challenge us. Plus we're the strongest nation economically."

"I hope so, Captain. But the fact that disturbs me even more is that Americans made the decision to drop the atom bomb on defenseless people in Hiroshima and Nagasaki, not on Yokosuka or Kawasaki or other military areas. They selected a peaceful city like Hiroshima...an overgrown town..."

The two had been sitting watching a sunset. With the war over, there were only a handful of internees left. It was not like the early camps, with machine guns and trained dogs. Now both sides were waiting wearily until they could close the camp and go home to their families. The twilight darkened, and it was difficult to distinguish a "white" man from a "yellow" man, a jailor from a jailed.

"Anyway, Captain," Tsuha continued, "no matter what happens, the U.S. is my home. My son was born in the U.S. I'm not taking him to Japan, to have what happened to me happen to him. I can bear anything...any sacrifice...for his sake. I can *ganbaru*, I can withstand any hardship. He's an American and he deserves to remain on American soil."

"Yes, Tsuha. Be patient. You'll get your citizenship back. It's only a matter of time. America is not a land of retribution, of vengeance."

The two men shook hands sadly, almost in resignation of forces too distant and too strong to penetrate, to question, to seek help from, to become a part of.

"Yes," Tsuha murmured. "People will forget. The government—which is really people—will forget. People like us, who will care about what happens to people like us? Who will remember me five, ten years from now?

Neidier Tsuha nor the friendly captain could know that Tsuha would remain a "man without a country," an alien in his native country, for almost half a century.

CHAPTER 21

THE RETURN:

Now, Where Is Home?

Rev. Shigeo Fujino—the priest who had passed news on to Mrs. Umeno Harada of Ni'ihau at Sand Island—signed his "no-no" papers at Jerome Family Center and his renunciation papers at Tule Lake. After all, how could a priest say he would serve in combat duty? So he was scheduled to be returned to Japan with his family.

He had signed away his citizenship so he could remain with his young children. Imagine his grief in learning that he was to be sent to Tule Lake while his wife and children would have to remain in Jerome.

Then, after his renunciation papers were signed, he was sent as an alien to Santa Fe Camp. "I'm an American citizen no longer, but at least I can go to Japan with my family," he consoled himself.

When he boarded the ship bound for Hawai'i, then Japan, he looked frantically for his family. "I won't sail...I can't sail, unless my wife comes with me," he cried. But all arrangements for his passage had been made and his possessions were already on board the ship.

"How do I get in touch with her in Japan? Where would she meet me," he cried in desperation. "Please, let me wait here and sail with her. There are small children involved."

The ship sailed with Fujino on board. Because they had been assured they would be sailing together, the husband and wife had not made serious arrangements as to where they would meet should they be separated.

In Japan, he was sent to a former high school, now used as a center where returning soldiers and sailors were boarded until other living arrangements could be made. Fujino watched every bus that entered the grounds. Would his wife and children be on it? What if they were sent to another assembly center? To another city? How could they correspond with each other when the buildings, in fact the city in which their parents had lived, were now leveled to the ground?

Fujino left messages on the blackboard by the assembly building entrance. He talked to people who came from overseas. He did not leave the center for fear of missing her. He read and re-read the newspapers carefully.

Finally, after two long months, 60 excruciating days, down she came from a bus, wan and harried, with three children hanging on to her. She looked as frightened as the children did. Fujino's love for them brought tears to his eyes.

There was little food. In fact, there was little food even for one who was rich and a native Japanese. Fujino had an older brother in Japan who owned a farm and home, and even he did not have rights to his own land because he had not been living there and raising crops on Nov. 23, 1945. That was General Douglas MacArthur's ruling, and many formerly wealthy landowners were now unable to get enough food to eat.

During the ten long years Fujino and his family lived in Japan they found they were neither Japanese nor American.

"You're not Japanese, you're American," the people said. There was subtle and even open resentment that an American should live in crowded and food-desperate Japan.

But to the Americans, he was a Japanese, with a Japanese face and speaking the Japanese language. How could he be an American? If he were an American, why would he have to beg to be sent to Hawai'i?

Fujino kept hearing stories of a lawyer in Los Angeles named Wayne Collins who had helped those who had renounced their citizenship to regain it. Who was this man Wayne Collins? How did one get in touch with him? Would he bother with a Hawai'i resident, especially a penniless one?

Week after week, month after month, year after year, Fujino haunted the American Consulate. He explained the situation to the staff time after time after time. The employees tried to avoid him.

One day, when he walked into the building he saw a young man, almost a boy, in Fujino's eyes. He looked like he had just been assigned to his first foreign office job, he was so eager to help and so sympathetic in his ways. Again Fujino explained the situation, and said that he wanted to return to America for that was his home, the place where he and his children had been born.

"Wait a minute! You say you're an American citizen but you signed a piece of paper and that ended your American citizenship?"

"Yes," admitted Fujino.

"Impossible!" the young man exclaimed. "You were born on American soil. How could you negate that fact? How can anyone change that?"

Fujino explained that it was during World War II, while they were interned in a concentration camp.

"Concentration camp?" the man echoed. "We didn't have concentration camps in the United States. We had concentration camps in Nazi Germany, not in the United States!"

"Well, maybe not concentration camps...internment camps? Maybe detainment camps? Is that what they were?" Fujino didn't want the man to be angry with him.

"Internment...concentration...detainment camps, what's the difference? The United States would never allow that!" He thought for a while. "How many of you were in these camps?" He seemed to be trying to test Fujino. Maybe Fujino had been in a county jail?

"About 115,000 Japanese..."

"115,000! Impossible! I would have known about it." The year was already 1955.

Finally, seeing the despair, the desperation, on Fujino's face, he suggested Fujino write to Hawai'i for copies of their birth certificate and to Washington, D.C. for copies of the renunciation form. "Bring these, and I'll contact others and work hard to get you and your family back to Hawai'i," the young man promised. He seemed skeptical, yet how different his actions from the older workers, Fujino thought. He looked like he was really concerned and wanted to help.

Fujino held little hope for a duplicate of his renunciation form. But to his amazement, there it was in the mail, after only three months. How unbelievable, that some clerk in Washington, D.C. had opened his letter, written in poor English, and set the machinery in motion so that a seldom-opened drawer could be examined for a rather unusual sheet of paper. From the millions and millions of sheets of paper stored in Washington, D.C. how had they found this form which Fujino had reluctantly signed?

At all the camps, no matter how difficult or unfair life seemed to be, one could exist if one had friends. Fujino, Soga, Furuya, Ozaki and

REV. SHIGEO FUJINO. After ten years of struggle, he was finally allowed to return to Hawai'i, his birthplace.

Photo Courtesy Shigeo Fujino

Chikuma had numerous friends. The secret, if there was a secret, was in caring and sharing—caring for one another and sharing both the good and the bad. That was such a hackneyed, over-used statement! Priests and ministers had been preaching that for ages, but now, finally, the internees realized this was true.

How trite—caring and sharing. They were sophisticated international businessmen. They associated with leaders of two countries. Most of them were wealthy enough to be independent. And yet, it was true. Caring and sharing—one's relationship with another, the ties with others—the family, the neighbors, friends, other businessmen—why, this was the most important and rewarding aspect of life!

"You remember when we attended Makiki Christian Church? By the time I shook the pastor's hand at the door, I had forgotten the sermon. Yet, 30 or 40 years later, I can see in my mind's eye Rev. Okumura talking about love and relationship. Caring for others and sharing joys and griefs—the way we are doing now in this camp—is this what the old-time Hawaiians called 'calabash cousin' relationship?" Furuya mused.

Yes, Soga agreed. In a democracy, in life itself, love is more fundamental than "equality of opportunity" or "liberty and justice for all," which the Japanese immigrants had been requesting of the plantation managers, he explained.

The few in the camps who sought isolation lost their reality and lived in a dream world of past or future. They became robots, programmed as to what to say or do. They preferred not to think, because of the futility of planning or because of the pain involved in thinking.

Throughout the four years the men were called by many labels: prisoners, detainees, internees, disloyals, renunciants, alien enemy, enemy aliens, Jap! But usually the labels described the person using it. Lt. Col. Rogers of Camp McCoy had called them "gentlemen" because he himself was a gentleman, a quiet and compassionate human being. There were those who categorized and stereotyped the internees as "disloyal" even before any individual had evidenced disloyalty. These were the persons trained to expect disloyalty, and any move by any Japanese was cause for suspicion. On the other hand, Robert L. Shivers, the FBI special agent in Hawai'i, had looked for and expected loyalty, and he had received it.

Whether branded "loyal" or "disloyal," it had been a long and tiring four years. But finally, in October, 1945, two months after the atom bombing of Japan and the end of the war, the internees received word the camp would be closed toward the end of the year.

Six internees who had gone to work at Kooskia, Idaho, returned to Santa Fe so they could leave with the rest of the Hawai'i men. 328 had left Santa Fe already, and now 42, including Soga, Furuya and Chikuma were ready to leave. Matsujiro Otani, who had been with them earlier and had been sent to Camp Amache in Colorado, wrote to say he had been paroled and had reached Hawai'i on October 24, 1945.

For some strange reason, the ailing businessman was sent to Camp Amache, a War Relocation Authority camp, instead of to Santa Fe with the others. Otani was scheduled to room with another man, but this person never showed up. Otani, ill, was unable to line up in the cold weather for his meals. There were no Hawai'i residents to turn to for help.

"Mr. and Mrs. Hiroshi Akao, a mainland family, took care of me when I was ill," he wrote from Hawai'i. "They fed me breakfast, lunch and dinner every day. They had five children and I would go with one or another of them to the Christian church on Sunday mornings, resting along the way. Sometimes I had a difficult time breathing, and the little girl would say, 'Shall I run get the doctor?' What a sweet girl she was.

"At church we sang the *sanbika* (hymn) loudly and I would feel good. Then on the way back, I stopped off at the Buddhist church to hear the Japanese sermon. I rested in the afternoon and at night, at 7 p.m. I again went to the Buddhist church because it was close by.

Sunday was the only busy day for me. The rest of the week I didn't do anything.

"Once I was ill at night," he continued. "But I couldn't get up. What should I do? How can I call for help? Then I remembered I had my cane leaning against the bed, so I felt around, found the cane and pounded on the wall next to the bed. The family next door, a Mr. and Mrs. Hatakenaka and their three children, came immediately to help and to get a doctor.

"When the officials of the camp found out about my health, they put me in with another man, a Mr. Wakatani. Poor Wakatani...in the middle of the night I had a terrible toothache so I asked him to get a doctor. He remembered there was a Dr. Kuwahara close by and searched all over for him. But when he finally found Kuwahara, he found Kuwahara was an eye doctor and not a dentist. Try to get a dentist in the middle of the night...all the barracks look alike and everyone is asleep. It's lucky Wakatani didn't get shot as a burglar or as an escapee.

"I understand you'll be coming home soon. We should have a get-together then."

On October 25, the day they received word they were to leave within ten days, the air was cold and crisp. Already there was frost on the grass and snow on the mountains. Santa Fe had been home for so long. Could there be nostalgia in leaving a detested internee camp?

The internees were told they would be allowed $30 spending money. The balance of their funds would be given to them on the ship at Seattle.

They selected leaders to facilitate the moving. Elected were Kazuto Takeda, Hawai'i; Kosuke Hirose, Maui; Masaichi Shinoda, Kaua'i; and Sawajiro Ozaki and Takeo Miyashiro, O'ahu. Acting as secretary was Minoru Murakami. Already they were so organized they automatically formed such groups so no one would have errors in the forms to be filled in English. There was assistance for the ill and elderly in packing and cleaning out the barracks. The caring and sharing was almost automatic by this time.

The next-to-last day was a day for beer, goodbyes, and autographs. They were happy to go, yet sad to break the ties they had built over the months and years. They knew they would meet each other again in Hawai'i but it might be different. They might meet as friends, not as brothers or calabash cousins. Titles, such as "Bishop" or "President" or "Board Chairman" could influence their ties and construct invisible barriers, or would such titles remain artificial?

On October 30, the buses to take them to the train station drove in. The men had taken a final picture a week ago, and now pictures and faces were matched as the men boarded the buses. The buses bellowed smoke, and the barbed wire fences, guard towers, and shacks receded into the background. There was absolute silence for about five minutes, as each man stared straight ahead, but at some unnoticed gesture, the men whooped with joy and broke into tearful laughter. Finally they were free and on their way home!

It seemed like a short train ride, although it was 1,500 miles from Santa Fe to Seattle. They could walk throughout the train and drink hot—not warm—coffee in the dining room, and even leave tips for the black waiters in their immaculate white uniforms. Of course they had to leave generous tips. Every little action expanded their happiness, their joy.

The beauty of Washington State, after the deserts of Santa Fe and the flat and desolate winter farmlands of Idaho was overwhelming. The mountains, the rivers, the evergreen forests were like an intoxicating drink. Furuya looked at the others. He could almost see *haiku* forming in some of them, as they sat with eyes closed momentarily amidst such beauty.

In Seattle, half of the men stayed at the Immigration Office, and the other half had rooms at the Seamen's Club Residence Hall. They felt like tourists, with their doors unlocked and a pool table in the recreation room. And, unexpectedly, they ran into old friends such as Yoichi

Hata, Rev. Ryuten Kashiwa, Taichi Sato, Hajime Nishimoto, Aisuke Kuniyuki, Usaku Morihara and Shigeki Yamada, who had been in Colorado, Illinois or New York. The stories they told were hilarious...now that they were free.

They had been promised their money—money they had earned or had sent to them from home—on the ship, and this time they received it, unlike four years ago when 172 of them had "lost" their $50. There was a total of $75,000 to be distributed. The largest refund was $1,700 and the smallest 40¢. The average was $250.

The immigration officers were amazed at the amount they had. "Your families back home must have sacrificed to keep you supplied with money," they said.

When the ship finally left, after six hours of anxious waiting, Kazuichi Takanishi from Kaua'i walked up to the deck. How different it felt from the time he had been shipped to the Mainland on March 20, 1942. Then they had been prisoners. Now he was unguarded, able to breathe the ocean air. He took some deep breaths. Suddenly he saw a group of American soldiers...was that?...was that?...

It was! It was his son Sgt. Takanishi on board the same ship. Father and son saw each other simultaneously and ran toward each other. They hugged and wept, then hugged and wept some more. Those around them wept too, but in joy. Soon it would be their turn to meet loved ones again.

Santa Fe, and all the other internment camps, would be a memory. The war and the distrust were over. All would be forgiven, no matter who had been wrong—the top-level authorities who had interned the mass of Mainland Japanese and the 1,500 Hawai'i Japanese, or the Japanese who could not help being proud of and had held on to their Japanese qualities. Not to forgive was to burn oneself out needlessly.

When the men returned "home," they knew in what country that was. The crowd that cheered them at the pier, the words ALOHA and WELCOME HOME held high over the crowd, the *leis*, the gifts, the tears, the love—all these cemented the knowledge that they were indeed "home." Had they returned to Japan, how would they have been welcomed? What about some of their friends who had elected to return there? What had their homecoming been like?

The street was lined with well-wishers, not only of the Japanese ethnic group but of many ethnic groups. Distrust, dislike and jealousy had mellowed after four years. A better standard of living for most, plentiful jobs, the exploits and sacrifices of the gallant 100th Infantry and 442nd Battalion, and the atomic bombing and defeat of Japan had helped. Where hatred of Japan had been transferred to the Japanese people in Hawai'i and on the Mainland after the Pearl Harbor devastation, now compassion for Japan's atomic bomb victims was transferred to the internees.

Hawai'i was home to the men and families, men who had whispered "*Ganbare, ganbare*" as they counted the days and fought and struggled to come "home." Their roots were not historic ones; their roots were nevertheless deeply embedded in Hawai'i.

Home was where one gave and received an unselfish type of love, the men realized, smothered with affection and happiness. Home—it was almost worth four years, to have this keen awareness of close relationships. Their bodies had been in internment camps, but their spirits had been in the hearts and minds of those they loved and who loved them. Was death similar to this? Was death merely a separation of spirit and body, and did it matter in what form the spirit expressed itself? Whether in a tiny white desert blossom or as a constant glimmering constellation seen as the twilight's first star? Need one fear death if one was allowed to play different roles in God's universal, time-unending play?

Furuya was at peace. Would Kazuo Sakamaki, Pacific War Prisoner #1, also find peace when he returned to Japan? Would friends and relatives who loved him welcome him as a human being and not as someone who had brought or not brought honor to his country?

"Sakamaki-san, *ganbatte neh*? Keep alive that spirit of yours! We Hawai'i people loved and respected you as a person. We are calabash cousins!"

And the Mainlanders, and especially the Panamanians and Peruvians...would they be allowed to return and find peace in their old homes? Or would they have to continue to fight battles as a "yellow" people in a "white" land?

"Calabash cousins! Yes, let's treat others as calabash cousins!"

Furuya no longer felt any bitterness for the four years spent at camp. Instead, he was grateful that he had had the time and opportunity to marvel at the symmetry, fragrance and texture of a single desert blossom from among the millions of desert blossoms that carpeted even the land behind barbed wire and watch towers. He had been able to sit with friends and try to count the infinite number of stars and to realize how small their one earth was. He had the opportunity to watch the perfection with which a spider spun its web. Patient, uncomplaining, it always depended on its own resources, even when its home was destroyed again and again.

Was the beauty of one flower similar to the beauty of one life, and each life had its own beauty seen by a few others? Was the infiniteness of the universe felt on a starlit night indicative of the infiniteness of some great power which really had no name because it couldn't even be imagined in man's puny mind? Was the patience and persistence of the spider a lesson to the way each human being must tackle his own problems? Soga, Furuya and some others had pondered these questions again and again.

The war had ended. A new life was to begin in an old environment. But they had had time to examine their conscience, their values, their objectives, and their relationships with others.

They had not only survived; they had transcended that which they had considered unjust. Their experiences were like the lotus blossom which grows in mud but which seeks clean water and sends its delicate blossom into the air. Even indignities could produce unblemished, fragile blossoms of great beauty!

But now it was homecoming time! Furuya smiled and waved "Aloha! Aloha!" as he stepped off the gangplank, following Chaplain Masao Yamada, the pastor who had served with the 442nd Infantry Battalion.

"Aloha! Aloha!" the crowd roared back, many with tears streaming uncontrollably.

Furuya spotted his wife, sons and daughter—was that grown up girl his daughter? "I promise to live with concentrated awareness to make up for lost years—not the four years in camp—but the 30 or 40 years I have allowed to slip by," he whispered as he hurried to his family waiting shyly for him.

The End

CHAPTER 1

1. Seiki Arakaki, sole survivor of the Kiho Maru, testified later that the skipper, his son Kiichi, and Kiho Uehara were killed almost instantly. However, where the skipper was silent, Kiichi had moaned once. On the strength of this testimony, Kiichi was said to have survived his father by a few seconds. This information was essential to the insurance company in determining payment to survivors. The company paid $8,000 on an insurance policy to the family.

   In 1967, 26 years after the incident, Attorney Clarence Shimamura instituted a request for compensation for the loss of the sampan and for the death of father and son. Earlier, Hawai‘i's delegate to Congress Joseph R. Farrington had introduced measures for such compensation. They were both unsuccessful.

   Skipper Onishi was also not compensated for his injuries and for the loss of his sampan.

   The writer is indebted to Seiki Arakaki, Kimie Shidaki, Katsukichi Kida and Mr. and Mrs. Sannosuke Onishi for providing interviews, and to a Dec. 7, 1977 article in the *Honolulu Star-Bulletin* and to a Dec. 14, 1977 article in the *Hawai‘i Hochi*.

CHAPTER 2

1. The 27 were Daizo Sumida, Wasuke Motoshige, Dr. Iga Mori, Dr. Tokue Takahashi, Taichi Sato, Eichi Kishida, Hideyuki Serizawa, Tsunetaro Harada, Rev. Chinpei Goto, Seizo Yamamoto, Junichi Fujii, Yasutaro Soga, Mizoguchi Komeya, Ryoichi Tanaka, Kazuhiko Ogata, Toraki Kimura, Sadasuke Hamamoto, Tomoji Matsumoto, Ryuichi Saiki, Dr. Saburo Hayashi, Hiroshi Tahara, Seiji Obata, Saichiro Kubota, Kango Kawasaki, Yoshihiro Sugamura, Koshiro Tofukuji and Tokuichi Miyazaki.
2. Ladislas Farago. *The Broken Seal*. New York: Random House, Inc., 1967, p. 239.
3. *Ibid.*, 239.
4. *Ibid.*, 239.
5. *Ibid.*, 314.
6. *Ibid.*, 315.
7. *Ibid.*, 130.
8. J. Edgar Hoover, "Alien Enemy Control," *Iowa Law Review* 29 (3) Vol. 29, 1944, p. 402.
9. *Ibid.*, 398.
10. *Ibid.*, 398.
11. *Ibid.*, 402.
12. *Ibid.*, 403.

CHAPTER 4

1. Moon, Thomas N. and Carl F. Eifler. *The Deadliest Colonel*. New York: Vantage Press, 1975. p. 19.

2. Roger Daniels. *The Decision to Relocate the Japanese Americans.* Harold M. Hyman, Ed. New York: J.B. Lippincott Company, 1975. p. 27.
3. *Ibid.*, p. 28.
4. Michi Weglyn. *Years of Infamy.* New York: William Morrow and Co. Inc., 1976, p. 174.
5. *Ibid.*, p. 175.
6. Letter from Helmut Emig. Courtesy Col. Carl F. Eifler.
7. Kazuo Miyamoto. *Hawai'i: End of the Rainbow.* Rutland, Vt, Bridgeway Press, 1964, p. 346.

CHAPTER 12
1. Michi Weglin, *Years of Infamy.* New York: William Morrow Company, Inc., 1976. pp. 183-186.
2. Suikei Furuya, *Ruten: Poems by Suikei.* Kamakura, Japan: Sounsha, 1957. (A collection of haiku from 1912-1945.

CHAPTER 13
1. Hekigodo, "Chilly Night," *The Japanese Haiku*, by Kenneth Yasuda. Rutland, Vt.: Charles E. Tuttle Co., 1957, p. 197.

CHAPTER 17
1. John A. Rademaker. *These Are Americans: The Japanese Americans in World War II.* Palo Alto, CA: Pacific books, 1951, p. 4.
2. American Red Cross. "Statement of Procedure in Connection with the Providing of Welfare Service to the Dependents of Internees and Detained Persons." An Occasional Paper. March 31,1942. p. 1.
3. *Ibid.* p. 3.
4. Bureau of Public Assistance, Federal Security Agency, Social Security Board. "Summary of Program for Providing Necessary Assistance to Enemy Aliens and Other Persons Affected By Restrictive Action of the Federal Government." April 24, 1942, p. 1.
5. Federal Security Agency, Social Security Board. "Policy and Procedure for Providing Assistance and Service to Dependents of Interned and Detained Persons." June 1, 1942. p. 8.
6. Gwenfread Allen. *Hawai'i's War Years, 1941-1945.* Westport, Conn.: Greenwood Press, 1950. p. 138.

Seiki Arakaki
Noriaki Atsuumi
Helen Y. Ayano
Sakao Baba
Masayuki Chikuma
Col. David R. Dingeman
Col. Carl F. Eifler
Bishop Kyodo Fujihana
Herbert K. Fujimoto
Hisashi Fujimoto
Rev. Shigeo Fujino
Mrs. Kumaji Furuya
Irene Umeno Harada
Cheryl Harstad
George Y. Hoshida
Chojiro Kageura
Nobuo Kageura
Tadao Kageura
Shimeji Kanazawa
Tomio and Irene Kanno
Katsukichi Kida
Otome Kishishita
Seiji Kishishita
Yoshiharu Kodama
Kiyoichi Koide
Judge Masaji Marumoto
Bishop Gyokuei Matsuura
Iwao and Michiko Michihara

Itsuki Miyamoto
Dr. Kazuo Miyamoto
Taiji Murakami
Paul S. Muraoka
Gladys Naitoh
Charles Koji & Yaeko N. Nakano
Dan Toru Nishikawa
Genevieve Okinaga
James K. and Jane Omizo
Sannosuke Onishi
Otokichi Ozaki
Joe Pacifici
Toshio Saito
Lawrence T. Sakuma
Kimie Kida Shidaki
Shigeo Shigenaga
Miya Soga
Col. Siegfried Spillner
Shinobu Taketa
Haru Tanaka
Henry T. Tanaka
Kazuhiro Tanaka
Rev. Kenjitsu Tsuha
Munekazu Ueno
Minoru Urata
Toraji Yano
Kazuo Yokota
Kiyoshi Yonemura

LIST OF INTERNEES
GROUP 1
February 20, 1942

Akizaki Takeo
Ambara Masashi
Araki Kazuma
Arita Tamaki
Asaeda Horyu
Asami Shoichi
Atsuumi Noriaki
Baba Tokuji
Deme Jyosen
Fuchino Hego
Fujii Seiichi
Fujiie Shoho
Fujimoto Kenkichi
Fujisawa Hideo
Fujishiro Utanosuke
Fukuda Teiichiro
Furuya Kumaji
Hamamura Kyoichi
Harada Tsunetaro
Hasebe Ichitaro
Hashimoto Manzuchi
Hattori Shigenari
Hayashi Tomoichi
Hino Jyosen
Hirama Teruzo
Hirashima Masaichi
Hiromitsu Eiichiro
Honda Eisaku
Honda Hiroshi
Honda Kenju
Hori Minetaro
Ichiba Isao
Ida Taira
Iida Koichi
Iinuma Toshio

Ikezawa Shuntaro
Imamura Tsutomu
Inokuchi Uyemon
Ishida Kyujiro
Ishikawa Kozo
Ishimoto Masao
Isobe Setsu
Isobe Jusui
Iwahara Taketo
Iwata Masayuki
Kabashima Suijo
Kagawa Takeo
Kashima Ryuichi
Kawakami Shozo
Kawamoto Katsuichi
Kawasaki Kashu
Kayahara Chosuke
Kimura Akio
Kimura Kenji
Kimura Muneo
Kimura Tomiji
Kimura Toraki
Kishida Eiichi
Kiyohara Tetsuei
Kobayashi Nisshu
Kodama Masayuki
Kohatsu Yukihide
Kojima Sadakichi
Komatsu Taichi
Konno Ichiro
Kubokawa Kyujo
Kuchiba Gikyo
Kuroda Keisei
Kurokawa Tetsuji
Kusuda Kakushin
Maekawa Shigezo
Masaki Jikyo
Masaki Shozaemon
Matano Kojin

Matsubayashi Shushin
Matsuda Ihichi
Matsuda Genichi
Matsui Totaro
Matsumura Tamotsu
Mikami Shuji
Miki Yasuemon
Mikuni Matagoro
Miyagawa Shintaro
Miyagi Genei
Miyagi Takeo
Miyamoto Kazuo
Miyamoto Jinpei
Miyao Shigemaru
Mizumoto Shigeki
Morita Koetsu
Motoshige Hiroshi
Motoshige Tatsuo
Motobe Ryujun
Nada Yujiro
Nago Ninryo
Nakama Genpachi
Nakamoto Hidekichi
Nakamura Koichiro
Nakamura Tomoaki
Nakano Tamejiro
Nakano Kyoichi
Nakayama Dengo
Niimi Tokuichi
Nishiki Kakujiro
Obata Soichi
Oda Hakuai
Odo Shunichi
Ogata Kazuhiko
Ogawa Yoshiro
Oi Jyoei
Ooka Suekichi
Okano Ryoshin
Okawa Gendo

Onoda Toratoro
Orita Isaku
Oshima Shigeo
Otani Genji
Saito Seigan
Sakamoto Masao
Sakamoto Sanji
Sakurasawa Heitaro
Sasaki Giichi
Sasaki Tadao
Sasaki Yoshinobu
Sato Taichi
Sato Yazo
Sayegusa Kinzo
Sekiya Kichitaro
Serizawa Hideyuki
Shigekuni Aisuke
Shigemoto Osuke
Shigenaga Kakuro
Shimoda Shigezo
Sogawa Masao
Sonoda Santaro
Sugimoto Seiichi
Sumida Daizo
Sumida Shinzaburo
Suetomi Koten
Sueyasu Yonezo
Suzuki Eijiro
Takahashi Rien
Takahashi Tokue
Takakuwa Shujiro
Takei Tsuyoshi
Tanaka Katsuichi
Tanaka Tamaichi
Taiga Suekichi
Tashiro Manabu
Tatsuguchi Goki
Takitani Genshin
Toda Taiyu

Tokairin Jinhichi
Tomita Kazuo
Toyama Takinosuke
Toyama Tetsuo
Toyofuku Hatsutaro
Toyota Setsuzo
Tsuha Kenjitsu
Tsunoda Kensaku
Ueno Sakujiro
Ueda Toraichi
Uyehara Saburo
Ueoka Sokan
Wada Umeo
Wada Takashi
Yama Manabu
Yamanaka Heiichi
Yamane Goichi
Yamane Seigi
Yamasato Jikai
Yonehara Ryosen

GROUP 2
March 20, 1942

Aka Kyosei
Akegarasu Takeo
Anma Takao
Asano Kakusho
Asaoka Kakuho
Asato Eishu
Chikuma Masayuki
Fujihana Kyodo
Fujino Shigeo
Fukuhara Nao
Fukunaga Zeichi
Furuya Kaetsu
Goto Mankichi
Hamada Itsuo
Hamamoto Sadasuke

Hamamura Chiyomatsu
Handa Tessui
Hasegawa Kenryu
Hasegawa Tsuruzo
Hayashi Kyuhichi
Himeno Seiko
Hino Shutan
Hirano Naojiro
Hirano Toshio
Hirayama Shinsei
Hirose Kosuke
Hisatake Itsuo
Horiuchi Mitsutaka
Ichikawa Kiyoshi
Ikeno Masao
Ikuta Seiichi
Imai Toyoji
Inasaki Itsuo
Inouye Jukichi
Inouye Kumaki
Iseri Torao
Ishizaki Raiji
Ito Choichi
Iwasa Sueji
Iwashita Shigeo
Izumi Kakusho
Isumi Kiyoto
Itsuno Tokio
Kajiwara Taryo
Kanja Yonezo
Kashiwabara Ryuju
Katoda Tetsuei
Kawauchi Kichitaro
Kikuchi Chigyoku
Kirita Kamekichi
Kitajima Masao
Kitajima Yoshio
Kiyosaki Masato
Kobayashi Enjo

Kobayashi Motoichi
Kobayashi Yoshio
Koide Shoichi
Kojima Hikoji
Kokuzo Zenkai
Kubota Ryudo
Kubota Saichiro
Kudo Isamu
Kuniyuki Ikuzo
Kuwahara Gunichi
Kuwahara Shigeru
Maeda Kametaro
Mamiya Toshio
Masamura Iwato
Mashimo Junzo
Masuda Gosaku
Matsuda Takahiko
Matsuda Ryugen
Matsui Kakusuke
Matsui Yuutetsu
Matsumoto Kazumi
Matsuo Umesuke
Matsuura Gyokuei
Matsuura Shuun
Miho Katsuichi
Miura Genpei
Miura Shinichi
Miyamoto Buntetsu
Miyazaki Hiseki
Miyata Koichi
Mochizuki Tanryu
Murai Masao
Murakami Minoru
Nagakura Eizo
Naitoh Kyogyo
Nakamura Kokichi
Nakatsuka Ichiro
Nakayama Hozui

Nishida Biho
Nishii Kokyo
Nishizawa Kozan
Nonomura Yuuko
Ochiai Ekichi
Oikawa Tokuji
Oki Koichi
Okachi Toyomi
Okamura Juichi
Okumoto Yoshimi
Okura Seido
Onaga Rincho
Ooka Hiroshi
Oshima Kanesaburo
Ota Gentaro
Ota Kiyoichi
Ota Kunio
Oe Hoji
Ozaki Otokichi
Ozaki Sawajiro
Ozawa Gigyo
Saiki Takaichi
Saito Haruto
Sakai Kunisuke
Sakamoto Kyuichi
Sakamoto Munetaka
Sakamoto Seiichi
Sakimizuru Atsuo
Sasai Akihide
Shiba Kakuo
Shigekane Juzo
Shimokawa Hanzo
Shinoda Masaichiro
Shintani Ichimatsu
Shiotani Motoi
Shirasu Jukaku
Shimonishi Iwataro
Shoda Seiichi

Sodetani Koho
Sokabe Ko
Sugimoto Tokikichi
Sugimura Iwata
Suzuki Sadaichi
Tagawa Shizuma
Tahara Hiroshi
Tahara Kameo
Taira Yojyo
Takaki Suekuma
Takanishi Kazuichi
Takei Torao
Takemoto Hikoju
Taketa Torao
Tamekuni Shonen
Tamura Makitaro
Tanaka Kyuhachi
Tanaka Yaroku
Tanji Shizuma
Toda Shoshin
Tofukuji Koshiro
Togioka Setsugo
Tominaga Asahei
Takushoku Giko
Tsunoda Takayuki
Ueda Ichiro
Ueda Kyoichi
Uenoyama Shutetsu
Umehara Shodo
Wada Ichiro
Wakayama Jitsuji
Watanabe Iwaki
Watanabe Tadao
Yamada Tomokichi
Yamamoto Kizo
Yanagihara Kanekichi
Yoshimasu Masayuki
Yoda Kichisuke

GROUP 3
May 23, 1942

Adachi Tokuji
Ando Shigeru
Arita Gentaro
Asada Shigeru
Awaya Shotaro
Bamba Genko
Degawa Rentaro
Endo Sutematsu
Fujita Sawaichi
Fujita Yoshiharu
Fujitani Kodo
Hagimoto Toichi
Hamada Kango
Hamasaki Yoshimatsu
Hanabusa Minosuke
Hanamoto Hitoshi
Hashibe Shinichi
Hata Yoichi
Hirano Keisaburo
Hirashima Kentaro
Hoshida Yoshio
Ikeda Chiei
Ikuma Kinai
Imamura Asatoro
Inoue Sadakichi
Iwasa Shinzo
Kagawa Katsujiro
Kaneda Yohei
Kanno Tomizo
Kashiwa Ryuten
Katamoto Usaburo
Kato Isoo
Kawasaki Kango
Kawasaki Ryosaku
Kida Katsukichi
Kimura Hideji

Kinjo Chinei
Kinoshita Ichiji
Kiyotsuka Tetsuzo
Kobayashi Shokichi
Koide Kiyoichi
Koike Yoshio
Koizumi Gensaku
Komu Mannosuke
Kuniyuki Aisuke
Kurakake Toraichi
Kuritsu Koichi
Kurita Yasuro
Kurohira Honen
Kurozawa Zensuke
Kusao Yugoro
Maehara Kenichi
Matsuda Rikichi
Matsumoto Yozaemon
Mende Tazo
Miwa Shogo
Miyamasa Kaichi
Mizutari Yasuyuki
Moribe Ryuichi
Morifuji Sadato
Morihara Usaku
Nakagawa Koichiro
Nakagawa Takehiro
Nakahara Buntaro
Nakamura Yuichi
Nakano Minoru
Nakatsu Tsunazo
Nekomoto Shunichi
Nishimoto Hajime
Oda Junji
Odachi Kinzaemon
Ohama Futoshi
Okada Jiro
Okamura Keiichi
Sasaki Tokuro

Sato Eita
Shigenaga Shigeo
Shindo Takuji
Shiratori Shunsei
Sueoka Tameju
Suzuki Genzo
Takahashi Hideki
Takahashi Izumi
Takamoto Wataru
Takata Keizo
Takata Toichi
Takemori Tamezo
Takeuchi Kunitaro
Tamabayashi Hiroshi
Tanabe Sannojo
Tanaka Kazuaki
Tanaka Ryoichi
Tanaka Tetsuo
Tatsuhara Koshi
Togawa Riichi
Tokushiro Nobuji
Uranaka Wasaburo
Wakimoto Katsuichi
Watanabe Tamasaku
Yamada Shigeki
Yamagata Heiji
Yamakawa Yoshinobu
Yamamoto Kazuyuki
Yamane Mitsuomi
Yamasaki Zenichiro
Yogi Seisaburo
Yonesaki Ushitaro
Yoshida Shinobu
Yoshizumi Kogan

GROUP 4
June 21, 1942

Higuchi Sakaye
Honokawa Keiichi
Ikejiri Daishin
Ipponsugi Riuichi
Isa Kashin
Isemoto Hisato
Kanda Michiro
Kanemori Shinroku
Kawahara Toraji
Kawano Kazuyuki
Matayoshi Shinjiro
Miura Mankichi
Miyazaki Kazuo
Mori Tenran
Nagasawa Shukichi
Nakano Yunoshin
Odate Chikai
Obara Kensei
Okamoto Kakichi
Okamoto Keiei
Osumi Sutekichi
Otani Matsujiro
Saegusa Zenko
Saiki Enichi
Sarae Tsuruichi
Sato Heikichi
Sato Katsuzo
Seiya Takeo
Seki Kosaburo
Shimizu Matsutaro
Takahashi Zenji
Takabata Yoshio
Tanizaki Hisatoshi
Tatsuguchi Zenkai
Toishigawa Hatsuichi
Wakugawa Seiei

Yamamoto Hatsukichi
Yamamoto Hiroemon
Yamasaki Katsutaro
Horibe Kiku
Kawasaki Miyuki
Miyao Yoshie
Miyao Yuki
Yamane Tsuru
Tanaka Haru

GROUP 5
August 6, 1942

Akimori Daikichi
Ban Keizo
Chinen Takahiko
Furukawa Issaku
Hanzawa Taichiro
Hataishi Kenichi
Hirae Kei
Hirai Katsutoshi
Hida Senyei
Horita Kyoji
Imamura Teizen
Isomura Takasuke
Ito Tatsuo
Kawamata Sadaji
Kimura Katsuzo
Kimura Toyoki
Koike Haruo
Maeda Hikoemon
Maehara Teiichiro
Maehokama Shobun
Manju Eiji
Maeda Yoshihisa
Miyake Eimu
Miura Takeo
Murashima Tateo
Murata Ryuichi

Nagami Genichi
Nakamura Tamio
Nakano Chikao
Nakayama Shu
Onodera Tokuji
Osaki Yojiro
Sado Takeshige
Sone Tetsunosuke
Soga Yasutaro
Tagashira Yoshio
Takashima Shigeto
Takei Nekketsu
Taketa Kazuto
Tanaka Hideo
Tani Shigeki
Toda Sosuke
Torii Ginpei
Toyofuku Shoji
Ueoka Isamu
Watanabe Yakichi
Yasunaga Tokuichi
Yoshimasa Kenji
Yoshiura Kenji

GROUP 6
September 16, 1942

Adachi Ichiji
Aoyagi Seisaku
Araki Tadaichi
Fukuba Kumaichi
Hirae Sotaro
Hirayama Unji
Ishibashi Gakuji
Izutsu Ryozo
Kisada Zenzo
Kobayashi Masaichi
Kusano Ishima
Marutani Matsuo

Miura Sadahichi
Mori Motoichi
Mukai Yoshizo
Murakami Junji
Shintani Ichiro
Nishizaki Nizo
Sakaguchi Toshio
Sekiya Yoshio
Shiigi Kenji
Sonoda Nejio
Tanisako Saburo
Tsuji Kokichi
Uehara Masayoshi
Uehara Yokichi
Yanagi Tokujiro
Yokota Kazuto
Ito Chuzo

GROUP 7
October 10, 1942

Arita Takazo
Hanzawa Tetsuji
Hasegawa Haruzo
Iwakami Konosuke
Kan Buntaro
Kawamura Shodo
Konno Manjiro
Kamino Tadami
Matsubayashi Shoten
Morimoto Tatsuji
Mikami Kakai
Murakami Shigeru
Okamoto Tokuichi
Otake Tatsujiro
Saito Yukihei
Suzuki Masaru
Takei Tokiji
Takeshita Kenichi

Takezono Seikaku
Tanaka Jitsuryu
Terada Shigeji
Yokoyama Shinajiro
Yoshizawa Jiro

GROUP 8
March 2, 1943

Akata Yaichiro
Arashiro Munehisa
Ashihara Sokutaro
Fujii Sunao
Fujitani Shiro
Hayashi Meijiro
Hiroo Jinsaburo
Hori Tokuichi
Horiuchi Takamasu
Ishikawa Masasuke
Kasamoto Mitsuji
Kato Yoshinobu
Kawano Shoichi
Kinoshita Takichi
Kobayagawa Tomikichi
Kawaomo Kakuro
Koyama Tomichi
Makihira Tamehachi
Matsumoto Kuramatsu
Matsumoto Toramatsu
Morita Zenkichi
Nakagawa Sawaichi
Nakaichi Yuichi
Nakami Hyotaro
Nakashima Hisajiro
Nakata Toshiro
Nishino Yoshinori
Onoue Hikohachi
Oshio Munetaro
Otsuka Hikoju

Takeshita Wataru
Takeuchi Naoji
Tanada Gihei
Tanaka Kanji
Tarimizu Tadayuki
Torii Chuji
Uechi Kenji
Yamamoto Tsuneichi
Yamamoto Yaichi
Yamamoto Yoemon
Yano Shigeru
Yonemura Kiyoshi
Kanazawa Katsuo

GROUP 9
July 1, 1943

Arita Nizo
Hamada Otoshiro
Horikawa Isuke
Itaya Torao
Kameoka Sukeichi
Kasai Ichiro
Kato Shu
Katsuno Asaichi
Kinoshita Hideo
Kobayashi Einosuke
Kondo Kikujiro
Matsunaga Nobusuke
Morishige Kenji
Moritsugu Yasuichi
Nakamura Ichiro
Nishiyama Kansuke
Nomura Giichi
Oka Wahei
Omiya Manjiro
Sakaguchi Kuwasaburo
Shimizu Kiyoshi
Shinohara Masami

Suga Mamoru
Sugiura Yonematsu
Suzuki Tajiro
Takahashi Umon
Tamura Giichi
Tamura Yoshihisa
Toyota Junichi
Tsushima Genpachi
Watanabe Zenichi
Yamamoto Toyosuke
Yoshida Hannosuke
Yoshioka Yoshio

GROUP 10
December 2, 1943

Asakura Iwakichi
Deki Ichiro
Genishi Ichiro
Gima Shimpuku
Hamada Takashi
Higa Kamasuke
Honda Gengo
Ichida Heikichi
Isobe Hakuran
Iwase Shiro
Kuniyoshi Asahide
Marumoto Masaichi
Nakabayashi Chugoro
Otomo Kenju
Okimoto Sakazuchi
Oshiro Hirosuke
Oyama Shuhei
Sato Giichi
Seto Naoichi
Seto Taichiro
Morikame Takasato
Tanigawa Tomizo
Teraoku Masutaro

Uesugi Hitoshi
Watanabe Akimasa
Yoshimoto Asami
Yoshimura Konoe
Yoshinaga Shigeru

HONOULIULI

Abe Kiroku
Abe Sanji
Akata Kyu
Akata Tsutomu
Akiyama Bo
Akizaki Yoshio
Aoyama Takeshiro
Aragaki Kiyu
Asakura Iwakichi
Asao Shigeo
Egami Jusaburo
Enogawa Seiei
Fujimoto Kisoo
Fujiii Teruji
Fujiki Tadashi
Fujimoto Shigeki
Fujita Kosaku
Fujita Masayuki
Fujita Yoshinori
Fujiwara Masao
Fukutomi Shinjiro
Furukawa Masami
Furukawa Shigeo
Gibo Anki
Gibo Eikichi
Goya Kandoku
Hamada Takashi
Hamamoto Kiyoto
Hamano Sohei
Hamasaki Yoshio
Hara Etsuji

Harada Shintaro
Harimoto Michinosuke
Haseyama Toso
Hashimoto Yasuaki
Hayase Ichiro
Hayashi Kenjiro
Higa Kamasuke
Higa Hideo
Higaki Bunzo
Higashi Terumitsu
Hirai Shinsho
Hirata Jiro
Hirokawa Katsuichi
Hishinuma Junjuro
Hori Takunori
Horita Shigeru
Idemoto Masao
Iida Tadaichi
Inokuchi Kakuji
Inouye Hideo
Ishida Heikichi
Ishida Kenji
Ishigo Inakichi
Ishikawa Seifuku
Ishiki Gyuro
Ishioka Yoshio
Itagaki Shigeichiro
Itaoka Seichi
Ito Iwao
Ito Kiyoshi
Iwahori James
Iwamoto Masao
Iwanaka Satoru
Iwase Shiro
Izumoto Masao
Jimbo Futoshi
Kagesa Shikatsu
Kageura Chojiro
Kageura Nobuo

Kageura Tadao
Kageura Yutaka
Kameoka Sukeichi
Kamishiro Noboru
Kanemoto Fukuji
Kaneshiro Masaaki
Kanno Sakugoro
Kawamoto Shigeo
Kawamoto Tatsuzo
Kawamura Daizo
Kawashima Masagoro
Kawazoe Zenichi
Kimura Kazuo
Kinoshita Masaru
Kinoshita Uichi
Kitano Masaichi
Kobatake Mitsugu
Kobayashi Yoshiemon
Kodama Yoshiharu
Koga Masao
Koide Hideo
Koide Yuichi
Komagata Zenkyo
Komune Heisuke
Kotoshirodo Masayuki
Koyanagi Fukuo
Koyanagi Kiyomi
Kubo Shinsaku
Kuga Hisaichi
Kuga Kazuo
Kumasaki Tamotsu
Kunimura Kichijiro
Kuniyuki Takeo
Kuraishi Tomoichi
Kuramoto Tameto
Kuwahara Tsuyoshi
Kuwaye Ryozen
Maemoto Isamu
Maeno Waichi

Matsuda Shigeji
Matsuda Toyoki
Matsumoto Masato
Matsumoto Shigeichi
Matsunaga Nobusuke
Matsuo Keijiro
Matsuoka Buichi
Matsuura Kakichi
Matsuura Toshiyuki
Matsuzaka Shigeru
Mihara Sensuke
Mitose Masayoshi
Mitsunaga Manabu
Miura Toshio
Miyahara Manabu
Miyama Masao
Miyamoto Isamu
Miyashiro Kaoru
Mizuta Tadashi
Mori Shigeo
Morikawa Heizuchi
Morikubo Shigetsuchi
Morimoto Uichi
Morishige Kenji
Morita Hideo
Morita Makoto
Moritsugu Tokuemon
Moritsugu Yasuichi
Moriyama Sadao
Motoda Chester
Mukuda Shinichi
Murahama Hatsujiro
Murakami Kamato
Murakami Taiji
Murakawa Masaru
Murakawa Takeo
Murata Yasumasa
Muroda Toshio
Naito Rikio

Nakaga Akira
Nakagawa Shiro
Nakamoto Tokuji
Nakamura Chusaburo
Nakamura Mitsugu
Nakao Toshio
Nakaoka Tayori
Nakashima Mari
Nakata Tadashi
Niino Katsuichi
Niisato Shigeru
Niitani Kazuo
Nishi Hatsutaro
Nishi Masashi
Nishikawa Toru
Nishimoto Goichi
Nishimura Masao
Nishimura Takao
Nishimura Yonesaku
Nishioka Hikoyoshi
Nishioka Kuniaki
Nishiyama Kanesuke
Nishiyama Kansuke
Noda Inazo
Norinobu Takeshi
Nose Masaru
Ohashi Mohei
Ohta Toshiichi
Oi Tetsuo
Oishi Kichiji
Okabayashi Toshiichi
Okada Isao
Okazaki Seishiro
Oki Iwao
Okimura Kazuo
Omiya Manjiro
Omura Sodo
Onoyama Ken
Omizo Kyoichi

Orimoto Kozo
Oshiro Shinko
Oumae Masato
Oyama Shuhei
Ozaki Ichitaro
Sadanaga Minoru
Saito Toshio
Saito Yukio
Sakai Futoshi
Sakakihara Tameichi
Sakato Shizuo
Sakuma Takeo
Sano Waichi
Sato Giichi
Sato Ichiro
Sezoko Shoichi
Shige Ryoichi
Shimamoto Seichi
Shimizu Masatoshi
Shimoda Toshio
Shimomura Kisei
Shinagawa Tetsuo
Shinno Minoru
Shinohara Masami
Shiraishi Tadatoshi
Shirakata Tamiichi
Shishido Genkichi
Suyemura Takeo
Suzuki Kazuo
Suzuki Seihei
Suzuki Tsuneo
Taguma Rintaro
Taguma Toichi

Tahara Jyoichi
Taira Kotaro
Tamura Iwakichi
Tamura Masao
Tanaka Sueki
Takahashi Shoichi
Takahashi Shozo
Takahashi Tokushi
Takahashi Yoshio
Takara Kometaro
Takemoto Seiichi
Takitani Kanichi
Tamanaha Tentoku
Tamashiro Shigeru
Tamayose Houn
Tanaka Henry
Tanaka Kazuhiro
Taniguchi Shinshi
Tanji Yukio
Tasaka Yoshitani
Tawada Shinen
Terada Kyozo
Tokumoto Eikichi
Tokumoto Mitsuo
Tomioka Sakae
Toyomasu Matsutaro
Tsubaki Edward
Tsuchiya Seiichi
Tsukamoto Kenneth
Tsukamoto Toku
Tsuji Tokuichi
Tamura Shigeo
Takahashi Naoichi

Uchida Kinji
Uehara Masao
Uemori Shigeyuki
Ueno Kenji
Ueno Takeshi
Uezu Yasumatsu
Urata Masaru
Urata Minoru
Wakamoto Giichi
Watanabe Zenichi
Yamada Kaoru
Yamada Saburo
Yamamoto Genzo
Yamamoto Gunichi
Yamamoto Kazuo
Yamamoto Kiyoshi
Yamamoto Koshio
Yamamoto Ryotaro
Yamasaki Hiroshi
Yamasaki Sam
Yamasaki Takejiro
Yamashiro Shusei
Yamazaki Giho
Yasuda Satoshi
Yonemura Isamu
Yoshida Goro
Yoshikane Teruo
Yoshikawa Yuichi
Yoshimoto Asami
Yoshinaga Sogi
Yoshioka Masuo

Allen, Gwenfread. *Hawai'i's War Years, 1941-1945*. Westport, Conn.; Greenwood Press, 1950.

Blair, Clay, *Jr. Silent Victory*. New York: J.B. Lippincott Company, 1975.

Bosworth, Allan R. *America's Concentration Camps*. New York: W.W. Norton, 1967.

Coffey, Thomas M. *Imperial Tragedy: Japan in World War II. The First Days and the Last*. New York: The World Publishing Co., 1970.

Conroy, Hilary and T. Scott Miyagawa, eds. *East Across the Pacific: Historical and Sociological Studies of Japanese Immigration and Assimilation*. Santa Barbara, CA.: American Bibliographical Center, 1972.

Daniels, Roger and Harry Kitano. *American Racism*. New York: Prentice Hall, 1970.

Daniels, Roger. *Concentration Camps USA: Japanese Americans and World War II*. NewYork: Holt, Rinehart and Winston, 1970.

_____. *The Decision to Relocate the Japanese Americans*. New York: J.B. Lippincott Co., 1975.

Davis, Kenneth Sydney. *The American Experience of War, 1939-1945*. London: Seeker and Warburg, 1967.

Eaton, Allen H. *Beauty Behind Barbed Wire: the Arts of the Japanese in Our Relocation Camps*. New York: Harper, 1952.

Edmiston, James. *Home Again*. New York: Doubleday and Company, 1955.

Farago, Ladislas. *The Broken Seal: The Story of "Operation Magic" and the Pearl Harbor Disaster*. New York: Random House, 1967.

Furuya Suikei. *Haisho Tenten*. Hawai'i: Nippu Jiji, 1964.

_____. *Imin no Rakugaki*. Honolulu: Hawai'i Times, 1968.

_____. *Ruten*. Kamakura, Japan: Sounsha, 1957.

Girdner, Audrie, and Anne Loftis. *The Great Betrayal: The Evacuation of the Japanese Americans During World War II*. New York: The Macmillan Company, 1969.

Grodzins, Morton. *Americans Betrayed: Politics and the Japanese Evacuation*. Chicago: University of Chicago Press, 1949.

Hosokawa, Bill. *Nisei: The Quiet Americans*. New York: William Morrow and Company, 1969.

_____. *Thirty Five Years in the Frying Pan*. New York: McGraw Hill Book Company, 1978.

Houston, Jeanne Wakatsuki and James Houston. *Farewell to Manzanar*. Boston: Houghton Mifflin, 1973.

Ienaga, Saburo. *The Pacific War*. New York: Pantheon Books, 1978.

Japanese American Curriculum Project. *Japanese Americans, The Untold Story*. New York: Holt, Rinehart and Winston, Inc., 1971.

Kitagawa, Daisuke. *Issei and Nisei, The Internment Years*. New York: Seabury Press, 1967.

Kitano, Harry. *Japanese Americans: The Evolution of a Sub Culture.* Englewood Cliffs, N.J.: Prentice-Hall, 1969.

_____. *Race Relations.* Englewood Cliffs, N.J.: Prentice-Hall, 1974.

Leighton, Alexander H. *The Governing of Men.* Princeton, N.J.: Princeton U. Press, 1945.

Lord, Walter. *Day of Infamy.* New York: Holt, Rinehart and Winston, 1957.

McWilliams, Carey. *Prejudice: Japanese Americans, Symbol of Racial Intolerance.* Boston: Little, Brown, 1944.

Melosi, Martin V. *The Shadow of Pearl Harbor: Political Controversy Over the Surprise Attack, 1941-46.* College Station: Texas A. and M. University Press, 1977.

Miyamoto, Kazuo. *Hawai'i: End of the Rainbow.* Rutland, Vermont: Charles E. Tuttle Co., Inc. 1964.

Moon, Thomas N. and Carl F. Eifler. *The Deadliest Colonel.* New York: Vantage Press, Inc., 1975.

Morgenstern, George Edward. *Pearl Harbor: The Story of the Secret War.* New York: The Devlin Adain Co., 1947.

Morison, Samuel Eliot. "The Rising Sun in the Pacific," *History of U.S. Naval Operations in World War II.* Vol. III.

Mosley, Leonard. Hirohito, *Emperor of Japan.* Englewood Cliffs, N.J.: Prentice-Hall,1966.

Murphy, Thomas D. *Ambassadors in Arms: The Story of Hawai'i's 100th Battalion.* Honolulu: University of Hawai'i Press, 1954.

Otani, Matsujiro. *Wagahito to Narishi: Sokushiki Hachijunen no Kaiko.* Japan: 1971.

Ozaki, Otokichi. "America Kenkoku Nihyakunen to Nippon." *Chuo Koran: Rekishi to Jinbutsu.* Tokyo: Showa 51, July 1.

Parkinson, Roger. *Attack on Pearl Harbor.* New York: Putnam, 1973.

Peterson, William. *Japanese Americans: Oppression and Success.* New York: Random House, 1971.

Prange, Gordon W. *At Dawn We Slept.* New York: McGraw-Hill, 1981.

Rademaker, John A. *These Are Americans: The Japanese Americans in Hawai'i in World War II.* Palo Alto: Pacific Books, 1951.

Simpich, Frederick Jr. *Anatomy of Hawai'i.* New York: Coward, McCann and Geoghegan, 1971.

Smith, Bradford. *Americans from Japan.* Philadelphia: J.B. Lippincott, 1948.

Soga, Yasutaro. *Tessaku Seikatsu.* Honolulu: Nippu Jiji, 1948.

Spicer, Edward H. and Asael T. Hansen, Katherine Luomala and Marvin K. Opler. *Impounded People: Japanese Americans in the Relocation Centers.* Tucson, Arizona: University of Arizona Press, 1969.

Taylor, Theodore. *Air Raid-Pearl Harbor.* New York: Thomas Y. Crowell Co., 1971.

Broek, Jacobus, Edward N. Barnhart and Floyd W. Matson. *Prejudice, War and the Constitution*. Berkeley: University of California Press, 1954.

Theobald, Robert A. *The Final Secret of Pearl Harbor: The Washington Contribution to the Japanese Attack*. New York: The Devin-Adair Company, 1954.

Toland, John. *But Not in Shame: The Six Months After Pearl Harbor*. New York: Random House, 1961.

_____. *The Rising Sun: The Decline and Fall of the Japanese Empire, 1936-1945*. NewYork: Random House, 1970.

Wallin, Homer N. P*earl Harbor: Why, How; Fleet Salvage and Final Appraisal*. Wash-ngton, D.C.: Naval History Division, 1968.

Weglyn, Michi. *Years of Infamy: The Untold Story of America's Concentration Camps*. New York: William Morrow, 1976.

Wolstetter, Roberta. *Pearl Harbor: Warning and Decision*. Stanford: Stanford University Press, 1962.

ABOUT THE AUTHOR

Reflective of Hawai'i's vibrant postwar literary scene, Patsy Sumie Saiki's writings express and examine the experience of being "local." Like the narratives of many of her contemporaries, her fiction often recreates a childhood idyll, preserving the memory of things as they once were. An acute observer of island people and their customs, her fiction and non-fiction portrays everyday life in fresh and honest ways.

Ms. Saiki is the author of *Sachie, A Daughter of Hawai'i*; *Ganbare!*; *Early Japanese Immigrants in Hawai'i*; *Japanese Women in Hawai'i: The First 100 Years*; short stories, "Communion" and "The Unwilling Bride," and the dramas, *The Return* and *The Return of Sam Patch*. She has also authored *Appraisal of Newswriting Classes and School newspapers in Oahu Public High and Intermediate Schools, 1958-1959*, and is the editor of *Renkyo no Ayumi: United Japanese Society of Hawaii 40th Anniversary Publication*.